A Companion Guide to the Welsh National Museum of Art

Edited by Oliver Fairclough
2011

First published in 2011 by Amgueddfa Cymru – National Museum Wales,
Cathays Park
Cardiff
CF10 3NP
Wales

© the National Museum of Wales

ISBN 978 0 7200 0613 1

Editing and production: Mari Gordon
Designed by: www.nb-design.com
Printed by: HSW Print Ltd

This book is printed on paper that is totally recyclable.
Mill ISO 14001/EMAS. RSC Mixed Credit, SGS-COC-000969.

Front cover: Augustus John, *Dorelia McNeill in the Garden at
Alderney Manor*, 1911

Back cover: Swansea dessert plate, enamelled and gilded by Thomas
Baxter junior, 1816-18

Foreword

What is the significance of what is happening now in Wales, where brand new galleries for contemporary art have been created inside the shell of a national building that is much loved for its architecture and cultural experiences for generations of children and adults?

At the turn of the 19th century and the start of the 20th Wales and the Welsh changed dramatically, economically and socially, and consequently in their self-perception as a nation. From this came the drive to create national institutions, universities, libraries, museums and a city before there was a capital city. At the end of the 20th century and the start of the 21st, a further change came about when a legislative assembly and Welsh government were voted into existence. From this government came the desire to rebuild cultural institutions not seen for a century. The crowning glory of this national public investment is that it came in addition to all the efforts and aspirations of private voluntary charitable benefactors and imaginative curators and directors, to create a fitting contemporary space for collections and acquisitions.

Today, under subtle spotlighting and comfortable air conditioning in the templar spaces of the new galleries we may reconceptualise and reinterpret Wales's visual art and sculptural production over four hundred years in their truly international contexts. As we gaze at contemporary art in cleanly designed spaces, we can view past works of art in a totally different way. Here we see everything, including ourselves, in a new light.

I hope I may be forgiven for selecting one example close to me geographically and physically, that of J. D. Innes's *Arenig*. We can now at last see Innes's colour-exploding landscapes of the mountain shining brightly as a Post-Impressionist in the context of the other continental Impressionists. We can view the mountain, Wales and the creation of which it is such a solidly essential part in a totally new way. Our debt to Oliver Fairclough and his colleagues for delivering such a vision is immense.

Lord Dafydd Elis-Thomas

Acknowledgements

This book has been written by the curatorial staff of the Art Department (see p. 176), together with Michael Tooby, Director of Learning, Programmes and Development and Bryony Dawkes, Partnerships Projects Curator. It draws on new research for gallery displays, and for the exhibition catalogue *Turner to Cézanne: Masterpieces from the Davies Collection* (Hudson Hills Press, Vermont, 2009), as well as on much work by former members of the Art Department, especially Mark Evans, Ann Sumner and Kate Lowry. The authors would like to thank current colleagues across Amgueddfa Cymru. They have also benefitted greatly from insights into the works discussed here from many people beyond the Museum, and received help on specific points from Ian Warrell, Greg Smith, Mark Evans and Krystyne Matyjaszkiewicz.

Publishing this book coincides with the conclusion of the complete redevelopment of the art galleries, which now form Wales's National Museum of Art. This is the result of a ten-year project to redisplay the art collections, refurbish existing spaces and create a completely new set of galleries for modern and contemporary art. For the first time, Amgueddfa Cymru has an integrated display of art, with a distinctive Welsh voice but international in scope, from the sixteenth century to the present day.

The redisplay began in 2001 with an extensive public consultation – at the time, a radical step for a national museum. This helped to establish some fundamental principles. These included the wish to show the art of Wales in an international context, and to create a distinctly Welsh narrative rather than segregate 'Welsh art' within the displays. Equally, the consultation affirmed the value of embracing contemporary art, informed by a new sense of confidence in contemporary practice in Wales. Finally, the displays were to be part of a shared ecology for the visual arts, in which Amgueddfa Cymru would work in partnership with venues across Wales, and with British and international partners, to ensure the collections and the visual arts of Wales were better understood and appreciated by audiences beyond the Museum.

The project cost over £6.5 million pounds, and received funding from the Welsh Government, trusts and foundations within Wales and beyond and an extraordinary range of private supporters.

This will not be the end of development of museums and galleries in Wales, either for Amgueddfa Cymru or for our partner organizations. However, the displays and programmes that we can now present in the National Museum of Art will generate new debate and appreciation for the visual arts alongside which new developments, including a Welsh National Gallery, can emerge.

A key principle of our new displays is that they are regularly refreshed and renewed. Even now, the modern and contemporary art collections are still much more extensive than we have space to display. As we lend and share the national collections some works featured here may not always be on display. However, such is the range of our collections that any visitor, at any time, will always be able to enjoy art of the highest quality.

David Anderson
Director General, Amgueddfa Cymru – National Museum Wales

Contents

Building a national art collection

This book is not simply a selection of the 'best' of Wales's national art collection. While it contains famous names and pieces of great beauty and value, the one-hundred-and-fifty works included here are also intended to reflect something of the character of an art collection that now comprises over forty thousand paintings, drawings, prints, sculptures, pieces of decorative art and works in new media. This collection has been in the making for over a century, and today reflects the changing views of the nature of our visual culture, as well as the shifting tastes and interests of curators, donors and funders.

It is also the product of Wales's particular history and geography. Before the nineteenth century Wales was on the periphery of Britain, distinctive in language but dominated by the culture of the centre, and artists from Wales trained and made their professional careers in England or beyond. From the late eighteenth century, as an area of great natural beauty, Wales provided inspiration to visiting artists from all over Europe. This dichotomy has led to a contested narrative about the nature and relevance of the visual arts in Wales that continues to this day.

The nineteenth-century industrialization of Wales brought dramatic growth; it created the iron and coal communities of the south and the north-east, and new urban centres in Swansea, Merthyr Tydfil, Cardiff and Newport. Contemporary concern over standards of design led to the establishment of municipal schools of art, including in Carmarthen in 1854 and Cardiff in 1865. Prosperity fostered a growing sense of identity and a desire for national institutions. Many of these were voluntary bodies, such as the Welsh Football Association (formed in 1876) or the Royal Cambrian Academy of Art (formed in 1882). It took the emergence of a block of Welsh Nonconformist Liberal MPs after 1868 to make public institutions such as a national museum a political possibility. Britain already had a network of national museums: the British Museum was established in 1753, the National Gallery in 1824 and South Kensington – the precursor of the Victoria and Albert and the Science Museum – in 1852, joined in 1897 by the National Gallery of British Art (now Tate). However both Scotland and Ireland already had their own national museums, founded in 1854 and 1877 respectively. In 1905 the Government conceded the principle of creating a national museum and a national library for Wales, and established a committee of the Privy Council to decide where these might be located (Cardiff has only been the official capital of Wales since 1955). Although Edinburgh and Dublin also had separate national galleries, the National Museum of Wales, which received its Royal Charter in 1907, was to be a museum of natural science, archaeology, history and the arts. Cardiff already had a municipal museum, established in 1862, which included a small art collection. The offer of this museum building, its collections, a cash endowment and a four-acre site in Cathays Park was enough to secure the national museum for Cardiff, while the national library went to Aberystwyth.

However, the story of the art collection begins not with the founding of the National Museum of Wales in 1907, but in 1882 with the Menelaus bequest of thirty-eight paintings to the Cardiff Museum. William Menelaus (1818-1882), the manager of the great Dowlais iron and steel works in Merthyr, had mainly bought contemporary genre paintings such as James Tissot's *The Parting* of 1872 (no. 65), but his collection also included several works by modern French, German and Belgian artists. Another key supporter of the Cardiff Museum was James Pyke Thompson (1846-1897),

William Menelaus
(1818-1882)

James Pyke Thompson
(1846-1897)

a director of the corn-milling firm Spillers. Because he disapproved of the Cardiff Museum's Sunday closure, in 1888 Pyke Thompson built his own semi-public gallery in Penarth, which he called the Turner House. He also bequeathed 149 watercolours including Turner's *Ewenny Priory* (no. 41), several oil paintings and some British and European porcelain to the Cardiff Museum, together with £6,000 for the building of an art gallery. His collection was to be reunited in 1921, when the Turner House and its contents passed to the National Museum.

Under the guidance of the Cardiff chemist Robert Drane (1833-1914) the Cardiff Museum built up a collection of Welsh ceramics, including the outstanding porcelains produced between 1814 and 1826 at Swansea and Nantgarw. In 1902 the Museum Committee decided to assemble a comparative collection of seventeenth and eighteenth-century English pottery. Soon after, Wilfred de Winton (1856-1929), a banker from Brecon, lent a group of early English porcelain. De Winton's great passion was the development of porcelain-making across Europe during the eighteenth century, and between 1912 and his death in 1929 he lent then gave the National Museum over three thousand pieces, completely transforming the character and geographical range of the ceramics collection. He was especially interested in the early products of Meissen (nos 20 and 21), the first European factory, and in Italian and Dutch porcelain. Meanwhile the Cardiff Museum had also commissioned Pyke Thompson's executor, the art critic Sir Frederick Wedmore (1844-1921), to assemble a modern art collection, which included oils by recent or contemporary French painters and works by several of the more progressive British artists of the day.

These precocious international collections inherited from the Cardiff Museum sat somewhat uncomfortably alongside the mission statement coined by the National Museum's first President and veteran campaigner for Welsh institutions, Alfred Thomas, Lord Pontypridd (1840-1927), that its purpose was 'to teach the World about Wales and the Welsh people about their Fatherland.' This duality is reflected in the founding charter of 1907, which stated the Museum's objectives should be 'mainly and primarily the complete illustration of the geology mineralogy zoology botany ethnography archaeology art history and special industries of Wales' and also 'the collection ... of all objects and things (including pictures engravings statuary and all works of fine art of any kind) whether or not connected with Wales' to further education and research. The Museum's first Keeper of Art, Isaac Williams (1875-1939), himself an artist, had therefore to care for an existing collection of modern art that did not much appeal to his own conservative tastes, and to build (with very little money) a collection that defined the art of Wales.

Isaac Williams took up his post in 1912, the year in which T. Mardy Rees published a biographical dictionary of Welsh painters, engravers and sculptors, which defined Welsh artists by their ancestry, and included many, like Edward Burne-Jones (nos 63 and 64) whose links with Wales were remote. This ethnic approach informed his first major temporary exhibition titled 'Works by Certain Modern Artists of Welsh Birth or Extraction' in 1913-14. Williams was supported by the Cardiff-born and London-based sculptor Sir William Goscombe John (1860-1952), a long-standing member of the Museum's governing Council, and an influential figure in the cultural revival that had brought the Museum into being. To them, the art history of Wales began with Richard Wilson, born in Montgomeryshire in 1713, and the 'father of English

The Turner House, Penarth
Designed by Edwin Seward
(1853-1924) and built in 1887-8

Wilfred de Winton
(1856-1929)

landscape painting'. The first major work of art purchased by the National Museum was Wilson's *Caernarvon Castle*, acquired for £380 in 1913. The Museum's canon of Welsh artists included John Gibson (1790-1866) (no. 55) and Penry Williams (1802-1885), who both made their careers in Rome, and the Anglo-Belgian Frank Brangwyn (1867-1956). Williams also bought prints, drawings and paintings of Welsh subjects, particularly portraits and landscapes.

With little money for purchases during the 1920s and 1930s, the National Museum was heavily dependent on donors. Goscombe John was the most regular of these, giving hundreds of sculptures, prints, paintings and drawings. As well as a complete representation of his own work, his gifts included that of many of his contemporaries in the British New Sculpture movement of the late nineteenth century (among them Alfred Gilbert's *Icarus*) (no. 68). Frank Brangwyn also made gifts of his own work, notably the monumental *A Tank in Action* (no. 110) and *A Big Gun in Action* in 1931. Another great benefactor was the Cardiff business man F. E. Andrews (1858-1943) who gave Welsh ceramics and a collection of mediaeval and later ivories. Interest in modern art had waned, and David Baxandall (1905-1992), appointed as Assistant Keeper in 1929, and a friend of the artist Ben Nicholson, had difficulty in persuading the Museum's Council to accept two watercolours by David Jones. However 1935 saw the organizing of a 'Contemporary Welsh Art Exhibition' by a committee which subsequently became the Contemporary Art Society for Wales. Shown in Aberystwyth, Cardiff and Swansea this exhibition was the first such major survey since 1913 and was dominated by the work of J D Innes, Cedric Morris, David Jones, Gwen John and especially Augustus John. The Museum bought from this exhibition, including Gwen John's *Girl in Blue* at £20, and Baxandall made a number of other contemporary acquisitions between 1936 and 1939.

The art collections had moved in 1922-3 from the old Cardiff Museum premises in the centre of Cardiff to a splendid new building in Cathays Park, designed in a severe Beaux-Arts classical style by the London firm of Smith & Brewer. Building work began in 1913 but was interrupted by the First World War and then by the Depression of the 1930s (despite additions in 1962-5 and 1988-93, it remains incomplete). Much of the cost was raised privately, and the most important early donors were Gwendoline Davies (1882-1951), her sister Margaret Davies (1884-1963) and their elder brother, David, later Lord Davies (1880-1944). Together they gave £5,000 in 1914 – rather more than the grant received from the Treasury – and the sisters added another £5,000 in 1916. Important though these gifts were, they are insignificant in comparison with the works of art they bequeathed after the Second World War, which transformed completely the range, scale and quality of the art collection.

Gwendoline and Margaret Davies were born into a family at the heart of the Liberal, Nonconformist and Capitalist elite of early twentieth-century Wales. Their grandfather David Davies (1818-1890) had pioneered the deep mining of coal in Rhondda. They began to collect art in 1908, buying paintings by J M W Turner (no. 53) and Corot (no. 72). They also admired the serious and melancholy in Jean-François Millet's scenes of peasant life (no. 75), and the wit and social comment of Honoré Daumier (no. 74). Their taste was initially quite conservative, including French academic painting of the mid-nineteenth century, but in 1912 they were

Sir William Goscombe John (1860-1952)
Painted in 1924 by Sir Luke Fildes (1844-1927)
NMW A 2566

The art collections of the Cardiff Museum, early twentieth century

converted to Impressionism by Monet's 1908 paintings of Venice. The following year Gwendoline bought Renoir's iconic *La Parisienne* (no. 77), and three of Monet's celebrated paintings of water lilies (no. 88). Impressionism was still little known in Britain and the sisters were among its earliest collectors. They were also among Rodin's most committed British patrons, acquiring nine large sculptures between 1912 and 1917 (no. 85). In 1918, while serving in France with the Red Cross, Gwendoline bought Cézanne's incomparable *François Zola Dam* (no. 79), followed in 1920 by van Gogh's haunting *Rain – Auvers* (no. 81), one of the first works by the artist to enter a British collection.

Gwendoline and Margaret Davies had a profound sense of social responsibility and hoped to enrich the lives of the people of Wales through a greater appreciation of the modern in art and music. They lent much of their collection to an exhibition simply titled 'a Loan Exhibition of Paintings' at the National Museum as early as 1913. In 1925 they lent nine paintings by Augustus John and these, together with four sculptures by Rodin, became a gift in 1940. In the aftermath of the First World War and the Depression, the sisters stopped collecting (although Margaret still bought occasionally until her sister's death in 1951) and concentrated their energy on their home Gregynog Hall, near Newtown, turning it into a centre for music, art and literature and for the promotion of international peace and social harmony.

The National Museum suffered only minor damage during the Second World War, but most of its collections were stored and many of its staff departed for war work. David Baxandall, who had become Keeper of Art in 1939, joined the RAF in 1941 and became Director of Manchester City Art Gallery in 1945. His successor in Cardiff was the author and critic John Steegman (1899-1966). Steegman came from the National Portrait Gallery, and during his seven years in Cardiff (before going to the Museum of Fine Arts in Montreal as Director in 1952) he began a survey of portraits in Welsh country houses, eventually published in 1957 and 1963. Post-war austerity was to cause the loss of many of these houses and their collections over the next decade. The greatest of these art collections, formed by the Williams-Wynn family of Wynnstay in Denbighshire, went in 1946 and 1947. Batoni's great group portrait (no. 29) of Sir Waktin Williams-Wynn and his companions in Rome in 1768 was acquired for just £230, while Mengs's portrait of Richard Wilson, given by the sitter to the same Sir Watkin, was donated by the Art Fund. In 1948 the Earl of Plymouth gave St Fagans Castle to the nation, to form the Welsh Folk Museum (now St Fagans: National History Museum), the largest of the National Museum's sites outside central Cardiff.

While the 1940s saw the breakup of many of the private collections of art formed in Wales in the eighteenth and nineteenth centuries, the post-war Labour Government expanded public support for contemporary art. The Council for the Encouragement of Music and the Arts (CEMA) became the Arts Council of Great Britain in 1945. Grassroots cultural projects in the depressed industrial areas of south Wales had coalesced into the Federation of Welsh Music and Arts Clubs the year before. The Arts Council was then a pan-British body, and seen by some as committed to a metropolitan model of excellence. Nevertheless there were many more exhibitions of contemporary art – the South Wales Group held its first exhibition at the National Museum in 1949 – and the subsequent expansion of art education provided new

The National Museum of Wales, Cardiff
Designed by Arnold Dunbar Smith (1866-1933) and Cecil Claude Brewer (1871-1918), begun in 1912

Gregynog Hall, near Newtown
Bought by the Davies sisters in 1920

opportunities for artists to live and work in Wales. The Museum was buying more new work in the late 1940s and early 1950s, but in other areas was still largely dependent on gifts.

The greatest of these gifts was Gwendoline Davies's bequest of 109 paintings, drawings and sculptures in 1951, which included not only her astonishing Impressionist and Post-Impressionist works but also a number of major Old Master paintings (until then the Museum had few older European paintings of any significance). The next twenty-five years, to the mid-1970s, saw the creation of a much more varied and broadly based art collection. The Keeper of Art throughout was Rollo Charles (1916-1977), who had succeeded John Steegman in 1952. The Museum's purchase grant increased significantly in a period of growing prosperity. A number of Old Master paintings were purchased to provide an overview of European art from the Renaissance to the eighteenth century, supplemented by loans from private owners. Gwendoline's sister Margaret died in 1963, and her bequest of 151 works reunited the great collection of modern French art they had formed fifty years before.

Gwendoline Davies
(1882-1951)

During the 1950s Margaret Davies, advised by Rollo Charles and John Steegman, had become a substantial collector of modern British art. After 1963 Museum purchases included major works by the principal artists of the day, among them Ben Nicholson, Francis Bacon and Graham Sutherland. This expansive period, ushered in by the Davies bequests, greatly extended the international character of the collections. Purchases of works by Derain, Heckel (no. 89) and Magritte (no. 93) in the early 1970s introduced the work of the *Fauves*, Expressionism and Surrealism. This period also saw a spectacular growth in the Museum's holdings of the work of Welsh artists of the twentieth century, particularly David Jones and Ceri Richards. The residue of Augustus John's studio collection was bought in 1972, and that of his sister Gwen in 1976. Each artist is represented in the prints and drawings collection by around a thousand works.

In 1952 the Museum's holdings of Welsh ceramics were more than doubled by the Morton Nance bequest. Born in Cardiff, Ernest Morton Nance (1868-1952) was the author of the monumental *Pottery and Porcelain of Swansea and Nantgarw*, published in 1942. His bequest confirmed the Museum's role as the principal public collection of Welsh pottery and porcelain. From the 1940s the Museum began to acquire major pieces of Welsh-provenanced silver. These complement the large loan collection deposited in 1922 by the Welsh lawyer and businessman Sir Charles Jackson (1840-1923). Jackson's publications, *English Goldsmiths and their Marks* (1905) and *The Illustrated History of English Plate* (1911) are the foundation of modern silver scholarship. In them Jackson relied heavily on his own collection, half of which was bought by the Museum in 2000, to illustrate marks and the development of styles.

Margaret Davies
(1884-1963)

Between 1980 and 2000 funding from Government, increasingly supplemented by the support of the National Heritage Memorial Fund and the Art Fund, made possible many major acquisitions – Old Master paintings by Claude and Poussin, a Monet of 1871, one of the Impressionist landscapes painted in Wales by Alfred Sisley and portraits of the eighteenth-century Welsh gentry by Hogarth, Reynolds and

Zoffany. In 1989 Graham Sutherland's foundation gave over six hundred of his works, and in 2002 much of the art collection formed between the 1950s and the 1970s by the Welsh Arts Council also came to the Museum. During 1988-1993 the existing galleries were renovated, and six new ones built. Collection care was transformed by the appointment of additional conservation staff, and the establishment of new stores and a Prints and Drawings Study Room.

Since 1993, the Museum has benefitted greatly from its partnership with the Derek Williams Trust. This charity has deposited on long loan the collection of mid-twentieth century British art formed by the Cardiff chartered surveyor Derek Williams (1929-1984). The Trust has helped make many purchases of contemporary art, and also continues to collect on its own account.

The collection of nineteenth-century Welsh ceramics grew significantly in the 1990s, and is now accompanied by exciting contemporary work in ceramics, silver and glass.

During the last thirty years Wales has undergone far-reaching economic and political change, in the 1980s with the decline of heavy industry and the scaling back of the Welfare State, and more recently with the devolution of powers to the Welsh Government. Ideas about the 'fine' arts have also been transformed in an age of digital access and mass culture. While works of art have traditionally been seen as timeless and to be enjoyed for their own intrinsic qualities, our definition of art has now broadened to include other art forms. Today there is a greater interest in the social, cultural and historical meaning of works of art, and a suspicion of the 'canon' – artists and their works seen by connoisseurs as being of especial quality and value. In Wales this has sometimes led to an emphasis on those artists of the past whose work is seen as contributing directly to Welsh cultural expression, and a neglect of those who may have been Welsh by birth or association but made little contribution to national life. In the 1990s the Museum was sometimes seen to lack engagement with its audience, and to be overly focused on the art of the past.

What of the future? The existing galleries were refurbished and redisplayed between 2007 and 2010, with a greater emphasis on the thematic and the flexibility for more frequent change. The Museum's purchase grant, unaltered for thirty years and eroded by inflation, was halved in 2011. Less will be acquired in future, even with the generous support given by the Art Fund and the Derek Williams Trust. On the other hand, more of the collection will be seen, and under much better conditions, than ever before. With the opening of new galleries for contemporary art in the summer of 2011, display space has increased threefold in the last twenty years. The art galleries now occupy the whole of the upper floor of the National Museum building in Cathays Park, to form Wales's National Museum of Art. Additionally, our programme of working in partnership with other venues increasingly takes the collection beyond Cardiff. However, the National Museum of Art is a half-way house. The creation of a larger and better resourced National Gallery of Wales remains a longer-term objective.

Oliver Fairclough

Ernest Morton Nance
(1868-1952)

Derek Williams
(1929-1984)

Sixteenth and seventeenth-century art

The oldest oil paintings in the Museum's collection are some thirty European Renaissance and Baroque pictures and a similar number of portraits of landowners, merchants and clerics and their wives from Tudor and Stuart Wales. Pre-1700 Old Master paintings are relatively few, but include several masterpieces of the highest quality. They range from Renaissance altarpieces to the landscape paintings of Poussin, Claude and their Dutch contemporaries. Some came from the private art collections formed in Wales in the late seventeenth century, while others were purchased, mainly between the 1950s and the 1980s, and illustrate sources on which British artists were later to draw.

Welsh portraits of the sixteenth century are generally by unknown artists or immigrant painters from the Netherlands. In the seventeenth century our portraits by foreigners are increasingly complemented by those of English painters. The collection of works on paper contains a notable group of etchings by Rembrandt assembled by James Pyke Thompson. There are good early portrait miniatures by Nicholas Hilliard, Isaac Oliver and John Hoskins, as well as seventeenth-century drawings of Wales by Francis Place and Hendrik Danckerts.

Sculptures include a group of French gothic ivories given by F. E. Andrews and Italian and Flemish Renaissance bronzes bequeathed by F. J. Nettlefold in 1948, as well as a portrait bust, shared with the National Trust, of Lord Herbert of Cherbury by Hubert Le Sueur, Charles I's court sculptor. The Mostyn ewer and basin (no. 6) are among a number of major pieces of silver commissioned by Welsh families before 1700. These are supplemented by silver, both domestic and ecclesiastical, on loan from Church in Wales parishes, and by pieces from the collection of Sir Charles Jackson, among them a rare complete set of thirteen apostle spoons made in London in 1638. Renaissance ceramics and glass are represented by groups of Italian maiolica and German stonewares. Seventeenth-century English pottery includes some Staffordshire slipwares and a rare Brislington dish (no. 18).

Right: detail from *Virgin and Child with Saints Francis and Lucy* by Alessandro Allori (No. 4)

1. Giovanni Battista Cima da Conegliano

(b. Conegliano, Italy, about 1459/60;
d. Conegliano or Venice, about 1517/18)

Virgin and Child
About 1500
Oil on panel, 73 x 47.6cm
Purchased, 1977
NMW A 240

This painting is a fine example of Cima's meticulous style. His methodical composition expresses not only the tenderness between mother and baby but also the figures' profound religious importance.

The Virgin Mary holds Jesus on her knee as if on a throne and the pair appear monumental against the small detail of the distant landscape. Jesus's pale skin and flawless features create an immediate focus beside Mary's dark blue and blood red robes. As he gazes at her face intently she looks down solemnly at his human form, reminded of his vulnerability and the sacrifice he is destined to make. Mary's marble seat and the parapet at the bottom of the painting also suggest the tomb where Jesus's body was laid after his crucifixion.

Such methods and motifs were heavily influenced by the paintings of Giovanni Bellini (about 1430-1516), who may have been Cima's teacher. The use of perspective and sense of movement in the figures are also close to Bellini's style.

The signature 'Ioannis baptiste Coneglianensis' painted on an illusionary piece of paper helps confirm the painting's authorship.

Although Cima was a very successful Venetian artist in his time, by 1500 his style may have appeared a little dated to some. His techniques were not hugely progressive and the statuesque rigidity of his oil paintings recalls the precision of older egg tempera techniques. Nonetheless, the solemnly devotional nature of his images was extremely popular among religious confraternities and more conservative patrons.

This half-length Virgin and Child is similar to other versions produced by Cima and his workshop, thought to date from around 1497 to 1505. It was acquired in 1876 by one of the leading art collectors of the period, Samuel Jones-Lloyd (1796-1883), Lord Overstone. *AP*

2. Amico Aspertini
(b. Bologna, Italy 1474/5;
d. Bologna 1552)

**Virgin and Child between
St Helena and St Francis**
About 1520
Oil on poplar panel, 85.5 x 71.1cm
Purchased, 1986
NMW A 239

Amico Aspertini criticised other artists
from Bologna for imitating no-one other
than Raphael. This highly animated
painting rejects the poise and balance of
classicism in favour of movement and
expression. The sixteenth-century art
historian Giorgio Vasari saw Aspertini as
a half-mad eccentric; however, he is now
considered an innovator in Mannerist art.

The complex composition focuses on the
familiar figures of the Virgin and Child,
who are surrounded by biblical and
symbolic references. The red coral
necklace Jesus wears is a traditional
Italian charm to ward off the Evil Eye.
The crystal orb below his right foot
contains a swirling mass in which tiny
figures refer to the story of the Creation.
To the right, St Francis's hand bears the
stigmata – the scars where Jesus's hands
were nailed to the cross; on the left is
St Helena, whose veneration of the true
cross is thought to have influenced her
son, the great Christian Emperor
Constantine. Behind, small figures enact
the Flight into Egypt against a windswept
horizon.

The monochrome frieze across the
bottom of the painting depicts Moses
and the Golden Calf, the Virgin and
Child and Josiah destroying the false
altars. This intriguing feature is an
imaginative play on the ancient carvings
Aspertini studied in Rome. In the early
nineteenth century the frieze was
separately attributed to Michelangelo,
and the rest of the composition to
Domenico Ghirlandaio. The painting's
expressive ingenuity is, however,
consistent with Aspertini's mature works
and Mannerist style, leading scholars to
date it to around 1520.

The painting also represents a milestone
in the history of British taste and
collecting. It was first recorded in 1816,
when it was sold by William Roscoe
(1753-1831), a pioneer in collecting
early Italian art. *AP*

3. Dish

Tin-glazed earthenware (maiolica),
painted, lustred, Deruta, Italy

About 1510-1525

Diameter: 40.6cm

Purchased, 1969

NMW A 30141

Plate

Tin-glazed earthenware (maiolica),
painted, Patanazzi workshop,
Urbino, Italy

About 1585-1600

Diameter: 37.2cm

Purchased with assistance from
the Art Fund, 2005

NMW A 37588

The portrait on the dish shows a fashionable woman with her hair in a snood. This idealised image of feminine beauty is probably based on workshop drawings and influenced by the style of local artists like Pintoricchio (d. 1513) and Perugino (d. 1523). This is a typical *piatto da pompa* (display dish) from Deruta in Umbria, a small but important pottery town that specialised in golden lustre decoration applied to blue-painted pottery.

The inscription on the scroll reads in Italian *TU SOLA SE CHOLEI CHE POIE AITARME* ('you are the only one who can help me'). This despairing statement of love suggests that the dish was a betrothal gift, possibly once matched by a second dish showing the young woman's betrothed.

The plate commemorates a marriage completed, that of Alfonso II d'Este (1533-1597), fifth and last Duke of Ferrara, to Margherita Gonzaga (1564-1618) in 1579. To mark the event Alfonso ordered one of the most spectacular maiolica dinner services ever made. Like this plate, each piece bears his *impresa* of burning asbestos – a symbol of undying love – and the Latin motto *ARDET AETERNUM* ('it burns for ever'). Below, recalling the Roman coins, sculptures and engraved gems that appealed so strongly to Renaissance collectors, is Fortuna, the Roman goddess of good luck.

More prominent are the fashionable *grotteschi* around the rim, most likely derived from ornamental etchings published by Jacques Androuet Ducerceau in 1550 and 1562. These prints were one of the main sources for the white-ground grotesque decoration that became a speciality of Urbino's maiolica painters from about 1560. The boar hunting scene in the middle is in the style of etchings by Antonio Tempesta (1555?-1630). *AR*

4. Alessandro Allori
(b. Florence 1535; d. Florence 1607)

Virgin and Child with Saints Francis and Lucy
1583
Oil on canvas, 258.5 x 167.6cm
Purchased, 1970
NMW A 3

This large altar-piece dates from the height of Allori's career. It was an important commission, a gift from Cardinal Ferdinando de Medici to Cardinal Felice Peretti (elected Pope Sixtus V in 1585), and was intended for a small chapel in his recently built Villa in Florence.

Allori's composition is extremely thorough in its religious symbolism. The infant Jesus is placed uppermost. The other figures, as well as the viewer, look up to his face, and his right arm is extended in a gesture of blessing. The Virgin Mary is second in importance, richly dressed in the traditional red and blue, and she wraps her child in swaddling bands. On either side, angels offer butter and honey in accordance with the biblical prophecy of Isaiah (7: 15). At the bottom of the painting the saints pay homage.

Saints Francis and Lucy were of particular significance to Cardinal Peretti. He was a member of the Franciscan order and was born on St Lucy's feast day, 13 December. St Francis is recognisable from his brown habit, rope belt and outstretched hands with the scars of Jesus's crucifixion. On the right St Lucy holds a bowl of coins, representing her dowry, which she gave to the poor. She was sentenced to be dragged across the ground by oxen, and holds a yoke. But the oxen could not move her and she was executed by the sword that lies at her knees.

Allori is sometimes thought of as a copyist of other artists, in particular Michelangelo (1475-1564) and Agnolo Bronzino (1503-1572). However this painting shows his confidence in the expressive Mannerist style and his ability to create a complex work. *AP*

5. Maerten van Heemskerck
(b. Heemskerk, near Haarlem, Netherlands 1498; d. Haarlem 1574)

Portrait of a Man
About 1540
Oil on oak panel, 39.4 x 31cm
Purchased, 1985
NMW A 234

Portrait of a Woman
About 1540
Oil on oak panel, 40.5 x 33cm
Purchased, 1985
NMW A 235

By the 1540s van Heemskerck was one of the most prominent and progressive artists in the city of Haarlem in the Netherlands, with many commissions from powerful clients. The identity of the husband and wife depicted in these pendant portraits is unknown; however, to commission the work of this artist was an assertion of their wealth and status.

While the couple's dress is fashionably understated, its quality is accentuated by the detail of van Heemskerck's technique. The woman's small gilt buttons and delicate waistband stand out against her black velvet dress. The transparency of her fine linen cap frames her equally pale and delicate complexion. Similarly, the texture of the man's fur collar stands out against his cloak and sets off his ruddy face.

These naturalistic figures and textural effects were continuing a tradition in Netherlandish art established in the previous century by artists like Jan van Eyck and Robert Campin. However, it was the influences adopted by van Heemskerck during his stay in Italy between 1532 and 1535 that made his work distinct.

Following the example of his teacher Jan van Scorel, van Heemskerck made extensive studies of both ancient Roman art and contemporary works by Renaissance artists such as Raphael. The effect on his paintings was striking. In these small portraits, the awareness of musculature and form suggests the influence of Michelangelo. Most telling, however, are the Italianate background landscapes that were probably inspired by the frescoes in the Golden House of Nero, which had recently been excavated. For the sitters, such references reinforced their image as affluent, modern and worldly. *AP*

6. Ewer and basin

Silver, silver-gilt and enamel, Bruges 1561

Maker's mark a P, the tail ringed and a scallop below

Height (ewer): 21.3cm; diamater (basin): 49cm

Purchased with the assistance of the Art Fund, 1977

NMW A 50490, 50491

Ewers and basins played an important part in the theatre of royal and aristocratic life in the late Middles Ages. They were used for the ceremonial washing of hands in warm, scented water during and after meals. They were also symbols of rank and status to be displayed with other plate on public occasions. Their use spread in the sixteenth century to the wealthier gentry, and this set was acquired by the Mostyn family of Flintshire in the reign of Queen Elizabeth I.

While the forms, especially that of the tapering cylindrical ewer, hark back to mediaeval prototypes, the ornament is in the new Renaissance manner. This comprises engraved foliage or arabesques, embossed masks in strapwork cartouches and swags of fruit and foliage. The ewer and basin were made in Bruges in Flanders, a European centre for the sale of artworks and high-quality manufactured goods in the mid-sixteenth century. They may have been bought there by a Tudor traveller, or imported by a London goldsmith. The arms of Mostyn enamelled in the centre of the basin seem to be an early addition.

The ewer and basin were probably acquired by William Mostyn (about 1518-1576), as his son Sir Thomas Mostyn (about 1553-1618) bequeathed to his son 'Sir Roger Mostyn, Knight, one silver basin & ewer parcel gilt, three gilt broad bowles with one cover, three parcel gilt broad bowles, three gilt cups, one gilt goblet with cover, two dozen of silver spoones lacking one, which said old plate is the old plate which were my father's and now remain unchanged at my house of Mostin. 'Roger's own will in 1640 also mentions '…the great basin and ewer which I found in the house of Mostyn.' *OF*

7. Adriaen van Cronenburgh
(b. Schagen, Netherlands 1525;
d. Bergum, Netherlands 1604)

**Katheryn of Berain,
'The Mother of Wales'**
1568
Oil on oak panel, 97.2 x 68.8cm
Purchased, 1957
NMW A 19

This portrait of Katheryn of Berain (1534/5-1591) leaves us in little doubt as to her wealth and social importance. Indeed, she was descended directly from the Tudors and features in the lineage of much of the Welsh aristocracy. This was why she was often known as 'the Mother of Wales'.

Katheryn was the only child of Tudor ap Robert Vychan of Berain and Jane Velville. Her grandfather was an illegitimate son of King Henry VII. She had many suitors, and went on to have four husbands and six children.

Dated 'ANo DNI 1568', the painting was probably commissioned by Katheryn's second husband Sir Richard Clough, after their marriage in 1567. He was a wealthy merchant and royal agent from Denbigh. The couple were then living in Antwerp, a commercial hub for luxury goods, including paintings. Van Cronenburgh's three-dimensional realism shows the technical superiority of Netherlandish artists over most British portraitists of the period.

The image also displays Katheryn's affluence. Her fashionable Spanish-style dress is patterned with intricate embroidery. The open collar and black fabric highlight gold necklaces and jewellery set with precious stones. Linked to a chain around her waist is a gold locket, said to contain a lock of her husband's hair, and also a prayer book.

Katheryn's riches and refinement are offset by a sense of reserve and piety. The most striking contrast is undoubtedly the skull under her left hand, known as a *memento mori* or *vanitas*. Whereas she expresses vanity by immortalising her own wealth and status in an image, the skull acknowledges her humanity and humility before God. *AP*

8. Attributed to Lucas de Heere
(b. Ghent, Belgium 1534;
d. Paris, France 1584)

The Family of Henry VIII: An Allegory of the Tudor Succession
About 1572

Oil on panel, 131.2 x 184cm

Accepted by H.M. Government in lieu of inheritance tax, 1991

NMW A 564

This painting is a piece of political propaganda celebrating King Henry VIII's reformation of the Church, and the peace and prosperity that England and Wales enjoyed under his daughter Queen Elizabeth I. It represents Elizabeth's vision of herself as the culmination of the Tudor dynasty and her concern with the legitimacy of her regime.

Henry is seated on his throne, and passes his sword to his son, the Protestant Edward VI. Edward died young in 1553, and was succeeded by his Catholic half-sister Mary, seen on the left with her husband King Philip II of Spain. They are followed by Mars, the god of war, symbolising the troubles of her reign. On the right, and nearest to the viewer, is Elizabeth, who had become Queen in 1558, accompanied by allegorical figures of Peace followed by Plenty.

The message of the picture is summarised in the inscription on the frame: A FACE OF MVCHE NOBILLITYE LOE IN A

LITTLE ROOME, FOWR STATES WITH THEYR CONDITIONS HEARE SHADOWED IN A SHOWE A FATHER MORE THAN VALYANT, A RARE AND VERTUOUS SOON, A ZEALOUS DAUGHTER IN HER KYND WHAT ELS THE WORLD DOTH KNOWE, AND LAST OF ALL A VYRGIN QVEEN TO ENGLAND'S JOY WE SEE, SVCCESSYVELY TO HOLD THE RIGHT AND VERTUES OF THE THREE.

Another inscription states that the painting was the Queen's gift to her secretary Sir Francis Walsingham (c.1532-1590), who is known to have had contacts with de Heere a few years later. De Heere, a Protestant refugee from his native Flanders, was both a painter and poet. He worked in London for several years around 1570. This painting later belonged to the artist Sir Joshua Reynolds and to the collector and antiquarian Horace Walpole (1717-1797). *OF*

9. Tankard

Stoneware, Siegberg, Germany,
late sixteenth century
Pewter cover
Height: 26.5cm; width: 12.8cm;
diameter: 9.5cm
Accepted by H.M. Government in lieu
of inheritance tax, 1996
NMW A 32753

Jug

Stoneware, Raeren, Germany,
early seventeenth century
Pewter cover
Height: 30cm; width: 16.7cm;
diameter: 9.5cm
Accepted by H.M. Government in lieu
of inheritance tax, 1996
NMW A 32747

Tankard

Stoneware, Creussen, Germany, 1639
Pewter cover
Height: 15.9cm; width: 16.7cm;
diameter: 13.7cm
Accepted by H.M. Government in lieu
of inheritance tax, 1996
NMW A 32750

German stoneware vessels, harder than locally made earthenwares and therefore more suitable for holding liquids, were imported into Britain in large numbers in the sixteenth and seventeenth centuries, and are known from Wales.

The tall creamy white tankard was made in the workshop of Hans Hilgers at Siegberg, near Bonn in the Rhineland. Its tapering body is moulded with three panels bearing episodes from the life of the Old Testament hero Samson (killing a lion with his bare hands, being seduced by Delila who took away his strength by cutting his hair, and bearing off the gates of Gaza). These are copied from engravings published in Nuremberg in the 1560s. The jug has a rich brown salt-glaze and comes from Raeren, near Aachen. It is moulded with a Renaissance arcade containing three quarter-length figures of the Seven Electors, the German

Princes who chose the Holy Roman Emperor, holding their coats of arms (1. Archbishop of Trier, 2. Archbishop of Cologne, 3. Archbishop of Mainz, 4. The King of Bohemia, 5. Count Palatine, 6. Duke of Saxony, 7. Margrave of Brandenburg). The shorter tankard has a brown salt-glaze as well, but is also painted in enamels. Made at Creussen, near Bayreuth, in Catholic South Germany, it bears the Crucifixion, flanked by the Virgin and Child and by the Pope on his throne.

These three are particularly fine and ornate examples. They were in the great nineteenth-century collection of Renaissance works of art formed in Prague by Adalbert von Lanna (1836-1909), and were bought at his sale by the Anglo-German diamond magnate Sir Julius Wernher (1850-1912). *OF*

10. Andrea Sacchi
(b. Nettuno, near Rome, Italy 1599;
d. Rome 1661)

Hagar and Ishmael in the Wilderness
About 1630
Oil on canvas, 75.6 x 92cm
Purchased, 1971
NMW A 9

Sacchi's interpretation of the biblical story of Hagar and Ishmael (Genesis 21: 1-21) is both sensitive and dynamic. It is the earliest of several versions of the same subject and its style is characteristic of some of his best-known and influential works.

Hagar was an Egyptian servant and mistress of Abraham, who was father of her son Ishmael. When Abraham's wife Sarah also gave birth to a son she persuaded her husband to banish the pair into the wilderness. Close to death from thirst, Hagar looks up to see an angel who points to a fresh spring and announces that Ishmael is destined to father a great nation.

Sacchi's painting was formerly in an oval frame but has been returned to its original octagonal format to reveal the full design. While the brushwork is loose and fluid, the composition is carefully structured. The angel's outstretched arm creates a diagonal with Hagar's cape, while the child's foreshortened arm gives a sense of depth. *Pentimenti* around the angel's head and body, where old paint layers are showing through, reveal small adjustments to centre and twist the figure. The general composure of the scene shows the influence of Raphael. Sacchi was one of the leading artists in the seventeenth-century resurgence of the classical style in Rome.

The peak of Sacchi's career and ability was in the 1630s, when he was working almost exclusively for the Barberini family. This version of *Hagar and Ishmael* appears in an undated inventory of Cardinal Antonio Barberini (1607-1671). The combined elements of boldness and control are consistent with works from the beginning of that mature stage. *AP*

11. Nicolas Poussin
(b. Les Andeleys, France, 1594;
d. Rome, Italy 1665)

The Finding of Moses
1651

Oil on canvas, 115.7 x 175.3cm

Purchased jointly by the National Gallery
and Amgueddfa Cymru – National
Museum Wales with the assistance of
J. Paul Getty Jnr (through the American
Friends of the National Gallery, London),
the National Heritage Memorial Fund,
The Art Fund, Mrs Schreiber, the Esmée
Fairbairn Foundation, the Moorgate
Trusts, Sir Denis Mahon and anonymous
donors, 1988

NMW A 1 / NG 6519

To save him from Pharaoh's order to kill
Israelite boys, Moses's mother hid him in
a basket of bulrushes on the River Nile.
Here he is discovered by Pharaoh's
daughter (in yellow) and her maidens,
who include the child's sister Miriam
(in white) who cradles him in her arms.
The story is taken from Exodus 2: 3-9.

The picture has a sophisticated
geometrical structure. Moses is at the
centre, within a circle of figures that
forms a pyramid, and divides, left and
right, into two equal triangles. It also
balances stillness and movement, rich
colour and shade.

In 1624 Poussin had left Paris for Rome,
where he immersed himself in classical
art and literature. His work is celebrated
for its erudition, but also for its clarity,
logic and order. Like Claude (no. 12)
he sketched in the Campagna (the
countryside around Rome) and his

paintings often include an idealised
classical landscape. Here he has located
the painting in Egypt by including
pyramids, an obelisk and a seated
personification of the river Nile. The
buildings in the background are taken
from a late Hellenistic floor mosaic
discovered at Palestrina and wall
paintings recently excavated in Rome.

Poussin painted mainly for private
patrons, both in Rome and in his native
France. This picture was commissioned
by a Lyons silk merchant called Bernadin
Reynon. After passing through other
French collections, it was bought in 1772
by Robert, Lord Clive (1725-1774) who
spent part of the great fortune he had
made in Bengal on a collection of
paintings. It passed to his son, later
Earl of Powis, and hung at Powis Castle,
Welshpool, and in the family's London
house in Berkeley Square until the
twentieth century. *OF*

12. Claude Gellée, le Lorrain
(b. Chamagne, Lorraine about 1600;
d. Rome, Italy 1682)

**Landscape with St Philip Baptising
the Eunuch**
1678

Oil on canvas, 88 x 142.2cm

Purchased with the assistance of
the Art Fund, 1982

NMW A 4

In the right foreground, the apostle
Philip, dressed in red and blue, baptises
the kneeling figure of an Ethiopian
eunuch. The subject is taken from Acts
of the Apostles 8: 26-40. Commanded by
an angel, Philip journeyed from Jerusalem
to Gaza. On the way, he met the eunuch
sitting in a chariot reading the prophecies
of Isaiah. When the eunuch asked him to
explain the significance of the text, Philip
convinced him that the prophecies had
been fulfilled in the life and death of
Christ, and baptised him as a Christian.

The scene is set in one of Claude's most
beautiful panoramic landscapes, which
extends to the sea beyond. With the
exception of the bridge behind the
eunuch's elaborate horse-drawn chariot
(adapted from the Ponte Nomentano near
Rome), this carefully composed landscape
is entirely imaginary. Together with his
older contemporary Poussin, Claude

perfected an idealised classical landscape
where nature is carefully arranged for
effect. His work was especially popular
in eighteenth-century Britain and strongly
influenced Richard Wilson, who urged
his pupils to 'rival Claude'.

Claude spent almost all his working life
in Rome. This picture was painted for
Cardinal Fabrizio Spada (1643-1717),
who had been papal nuncio in Turin in
1672-4, where he was successful in
converting to Catholicism some of the
region's Calvinists. Its subject probably
refers to this missionary activity. The
painting left Italy in 1798, and was later
owned by William Beckford (1759-1844),
the Gothic novelist and creator of
Fonthill Abbey. The industrialist and
Liberal politician Wentworth Beaumont
(1829-1907) bought it in 1865. *OF*

13. Le Nain brothers
(Antoine (about 1600-1649),
Louis (about 1600-1649) and
Mathieu (1607-1677)
b. Laon, France; d. Paris)

A Quarrel
About 1640
Oil on canvas, 75.5 x 93cm
Accepted by H.M. Government in lieu
of inheritance tax, 1968
NMW A 27

The three Le Nain brothers ran a
workshop together in Paris. There are
only sixteen known signed works by the
brothers, none of which use a first name.
This painting is one example, inscribed
'Le Nain Pinxit' and indistinctly dated
'164...'. Traditionally it has been
attributed to Mathieu, but there is
no firm evidence to distinguish any
of the individual artists' works.

Inn scenes with gamblers and dubious
characters were a common subject in
seventeenth-century art. Soldiers were
often involved, perceived as transients
with an appetite for fighting. Even in
the nineteenth century some artists still
returned to the subject, for example
Ernest Meissonier in *Innocents and
Card Sharpers* (no. 73).

This painting, however, is especially
animated with a dramatic tension rarely
equalled, even in their own works.

The Le Nains' figures usually stand or
sit in a static position, but here they are
depicted mid-movement. A young man
brandishes his dagger as his friend
playing cards turns pale at the horror of
his defeat. The other men seem unaware
of the attack apart from the central figure
who glances warily with his hands
bracing a half-drawn sword.

The realism of the Le Nains' peasant
scenes derives little from the art of their
native France. Although they moved in
the highest circles of the Paris art world,
A Quarrel appears at first closer to the
Dutch realists of the 1620s and 1630s.
However, while Dutch paintings usually
conveyed a moral anecdote, the scene
enacted here has no obvious conclusion.
The emphasis on the theatrical moment
and the dramatic shadow and light may
refer instead to the non-classical
Italianate art of the time. *AP*

14. Jan van de Cappelle
(b. Amsterdam, The Netherlands 1624;
d. Amsterdam 1679)

A Calm
1654

Oil on canvas, 110 x 148.2cm

Purchased with the assistance of the
National Heritage Memorial Fund, the
Art Fund, the J. Paul Getty Jnr Charitable
Trust, and other donors, 1994

NMW A 2754

This is one of the seventeenth century's greatest marine paintings. It depicts a group of coasting vessels off shore on a windless day. An important person is being rowed from a 'State yacht' towards the fortified town at the right. In the foreground soldiers celebrate on the deck of a ferry loaded with field guns and military supplies. The horizon is unusually low, and the great cloud formations are reflected in the mirror-like sea. The scene is lit by a muted misty light from the left.

Van de Cappelle was a largely self-taught and amateur painter. He spent most of his time managing his family's large dyeworks in Amsterdam, and his output of pictures was comparatively small. A member of the city's wealthy elite, he owned several houses and a great art collection, including seven paintings and

over five hundred drawings by his friend Rembrandt. He specialised in seascapes and *A Calm* is typical of his interest in light and atmospheric effects.

Dutch paintings of the seventeenth-century 'Golden Age' were much admired by British collectors a hundred years later. *A Calm* was acquired in 1763 by Sir Lawrence Dundas (1712-1781), a Scot who had made a great fortune from supplying food and equipment to the British Army during the recent Seven Years' War. Dundas was also a client of Robert Adam (no. 31), who remodelled his London house. In a painting by Zoffany of Dundas and his grandson in the library, *A Calm* hangs over the mantelpiece flanked by paintings by Cuyp, van de Velde, Pynacker and Veronese. *OF*

15. Isaac Oliver
(b. Rouen, France about 1560;
d. London 1617)

Henry, Prince of Wales (1594-1612)
Watercolour on vellum 6.4. x 5.1cm,
ivory case
Purchased, 1975
NMW A 718

To his contemporaries, Henry Frederick Stuart was the very paragon of a prince. The eldest son of James I (1566-1625) and Anne of Denmark (1574-1619), he was intelligent, erudite, athletic, moral and an excellent swordsman. He collected Netherlandish and Italian pictures and sculpture, as well as books, coins and medals. His religious sympathies were robustly Protestant, making him the focus of popular support. As in the majority of his portraits, Henry is shown here wearing the blue ribbon of the Order of the Garter, with which he was invested in July 1603.

Henry's sudden death at the age of eighteen was a cause for national mourning. The black background to this miniature suggests it is a posthumous likeness, possibly made with the assistance of Oliver's son, Peter (about 1594-1647). It was probably taken from an outstanding portrait by Oliver, now in the Royal Collection, executed between 1610 and 1612. The artist's monogram 'IO' can be seen above the sitter's right shoulder.

The son of a Huguenot goldsmith, Oliver came to England with his family to escape religious persecution. He learnt the art of 'limning', or miniature painting, from Nicholas Hilliard (1547-1619), miniaturist to Elizabeth I and the pre-eminent master of the medium. Oliver travelled to Italy in 1596 and his knowledge of European art made him an influential figure back in Britain. By the 1590s he was a formidable competitor for commissions with Hilliard and eventually outshone him in the court's favour. *CT*

16. British School, seventeenth century

Sir Thomas Mansel and his wife Jane
About 1625
Oil on canvas, 121 x 125cm
Purchased, 1984
NMW A 16

Sir Thomas Mansel (1556-1631) and his second wife Jane Pole are shown holding hands in a display of marital affection unusual in seventeenth-century portraiture. The flower in Lady Mansel's right hand is a marigold, perhaps a reference to the couple's young daughter Mary, but also a symbol of fidelity and devotion. They are both dressed in expensive black fabrics heavily embroidered with gold thread, and she has three ropes of pearls hanging from her shoulders. The large ruffs, however, were more common in the previous generation, suggesting the taste of an older couple.

The Mansels were one of the wealthiest families in south Wales. Thomas travelled in Italy in the 1570s, and inherited the Margam, Oxwich and Penrice estates in Glamorgan from his father in 1584.

Country gentlemen like Mansel governed their localities on behalf of the Elizabethan state, and he held a string of public appointments as sheriff, deputy lieutenant and chamberlain of south Wales. He was Member of Parliament for Glamorgan from 1597, and purchased a baronetcy in 1611. He made the former monastery at Margam into a 'fair and sumptuous house', and also had a house in London.

Thomas and Jane Mansel stand stiffly against a neutral background. The artist is unknown, but he painted in the formal hieratic manner common among British artists of the Jacobean period, delighting in the richness of embroidery and the detail of lace. Unusually at this date, and perhaps because of the painting's relatively large size, he used a stretched canvas, rather than an oak panel. *OF*

17. Francis Place
(b. Durham 1647; d. York 1728)

Pembroke
1678
Watercolour and ink on paper.
9.7 x 31.6cm (span of two sheets)
Purchased, 1931
NMW A 16371

This work (top) is two joined pages from a sketchbook. It is one of eighteen sheets by Place in the Museum's collection, fifteen of which are views in Wales. Ten come from one sketchbook made on a tour of Wales in 1678. They are among the earliest images of Wales in the collection. There is a crease running down on the right hand side of the page. If folded over, this section matches up with a sketch on the back of the sheet, extending the view. The bottom image shows how the whole panorama would look. The Museum also owns a larger, worked up version of this same view (NMW A 16370).

This view looks south, with the castle shown on a ridge at the head of a tidal creek. Much of the castle was destroyed by Cromwell following the 1648 siege. The round keep visible here survives and is one of the finest in Europe. There are several simple inscriptions within the image. 'Lion' on the left may refer to the Lion Hotel, perhaps where Place stayed. The church directly underneath this is St Mary's. In the centre is 'Pembroke Castle' and on the verso 'St Daniels', referencing a hilltop church not actually visible in this drawing. The buildings directly underneath this inscription are in fact Monkton Priory.

Place was primarily concerned with topographical accuracy, but he is also interested in creating aesthetic appeal. He was born into a wealthy Yorkshire family and initially studied law at Gray's Inn in London, returning home during the Great Plague in 1665. By then he had already developed an interest in art and printmaking through his friendship with the Bohemian artist Wenceslaus Hollar (1607-1677). He made many sketching trips around the country, some with his friend William Lodge. *BM*

18. Dish

Earthenware with slip-trailed decoration, Ralph Toft, Staffordshire

1663-1688

Diameter: 47.2cm

Purchased, 1903

NMW A 32738

Dish

Tin-glazed earthenware, Brislington, near Bristol

1680-90

Diameter: 35cm

Purchased, 1904

NMW A 34779

These two large dishes are superb examples of late seventeenth-century English pottery. The rare dish by Ralph Toft is a type called slipware after its distinctive, idiosyncratic decoration. Slipware was made across England, with the most impressive examples produced in Staffordshire. The decoration is achieved using different coloured slips – clay mixed with water to the consistency of cream. A dark brown slip has been trailed over the surface to create the outline of the design, in this instance a double-headed eagle. Other colours have been incorporated using orange and white slips and a yellow lead-glaze.

The second dish is a remarkable example of delftware, so called as it was inspired by Dutch tin-glazed earthenware, which was imported into Britain from the mid-sixteenth century. It represents an attempt to produce something akin to expensive Chinese porcelain, though the likeness was superficial. The thick tin-glaze provided a white ground for decoration, but was easily chipped and opaque, rather than translucent.

This dish was made at Brislington and commemorates the kidnapping of conjoined twins Prisilla and Aquila, born in May 1680 at Ile Brewers, Somerset. At this time, the lack of understanding and rarity of conjoined twins meant that they could be treated as public spectacles. Several pamphlets from this period report the birth of conjoined twins in graphic detail. Prisilla and Aquila were described as 'a monstrous female childe … so prodigiously strange'.

Shortly after their birth, the twins were taken from their parents by two Somerset squires, Sir Edmund Phelips of Montacute and Captain Henry Walrond, who sought to profit from exhibiting the twins. *RC*

19. Sideboard dish and ewer

Silver gilt, London 1693-4 and 1691-2

Maker's mark of Robert Cooper

Height: 4.8cm; diameter: 63.5cm (dish)

Height: 24.6cm (ewer)

Purchased with the assistance of
the Art Fund, 1945

NMW A 50305, 50306

Unlike the Mostyn ewer and basin of
around 1561 (no. 6) this sideboard dish
and its accompanying ewer are purely
for display. When forks were in every
day use it was no longer necessary for
the great to rinse their hands between
the courses of a dinner. The dish, which
is too shallow to hold water, was
intended simply to impress. Its only
purpose is to display the coat of arms of
its owner, Sir John Trevor (about 1637-
1717) of Brynkinallt, Denbighshire, and
of his wife Jane Mostyn, in a Baroque
cartouche of scrollwork and ribbon-tied
laurel festoons.

In 1693 Trevor was at the peak of a
highly successful career. A Welsh lawyer
like his friend and cousin Judge Jeffreys
(1645-1689), he ingratiated himself at the
court of Charles II and was an MP from

1673. Political and legal success followed,
and in 1685 he was elected Speaker and
made Master of the Rolls. He lost his
posts when James II was replaced by
William III and Mary II in 1688, but was
too useful to exclude from office. This
dish and ewer were acquired after Trevor
regained the Mastership of the Rolls in
1693 but he was deposed as Speaker
for corruption in 1695. His legal career
continued, and at his death he is said
to have left the then massive fortune
of £60,000.

Trevor assembled a large collection of
silver. Both these pieces bear the mark
of Robert Cooper, one of the best
silversmiths of the period. He apparently
paired the dish with a ewer of a couple
of years before. *OF*

Eighteenth-century art

The Museum's collection of eighteenth-century art reflects the transformation of the visual arts in Britain, as the country moved from an artistic backwater to one with a sophisticated art market, where painting was becoming a respected profession. Central to our story are two Welshmen – the landscape painter Richard Wilson (1713-1782), and the patron and collector Sir Watkin Williams-Wynn (1749-1789). There are over forty paintings by or after Wilson in the collection, ranging from portraits of the 1740s to landscape and history paintings of the 1760s and 1770s, in addition to drawings and engravings. Another focus is one of Wilson's pupils, Thomas Jones (1742-1803) of Pencerrig, best known today for his almost photographic oil studies of buildings in Naples.

Many works recall the Grand Tour of southern Europe made by both patrons and artists alike. Italian painting of the eighteenth century is represented by Canaletto, Guardi, Batoni and Domenico Tiepolo, and that of British artists in Italy by Joseph Wright, George Romney and Thomas Patch. The collection is rich in eighteenth-century portraits by Hogarth and his successors. We have four works by Sir Joshua Reynolds, among them his great portrait of Charlotte Williams-Wynn and her children, while those of his rival Thomas Gainsborough include *Rocky Wooded Landscape with Rustic Lovers*. Wilson painted in Wales, and his example and the theories of the Picturesque movement brought others, most of whom worked here in watercolour, among them Paul Sandby, Thomas Girtin, J.C. Ibbetson and J.M.W. Turner.

Sir Watkin Williams-Wynn commissioned neo-classical silver and furniture from Robert Adam. His 'great table service' contrasts with the rococo toilet service made for his wife Henrietta. Silver made for other Welsh families provides an overview of design from baroque grandeur to neo-classical refinement. Thanks to the generosity of Wilfred de Winton, the Museum has one of the world's great collections of European porcelain. It is especially strong in the early porcelains made at Meissen around 1710 to 1730, but also contains wares from most other German factories and those in Italy, the Netherlands and France. The continental porcelains are complemented by large holdings of British ceramics, which illustrate the transformation of the English pottery industry by Josiah Wedgwood and his contemporaries, and the concurrent spread of porcelain manufacture.

Right: detail from *Buildings in Naples* by Thomas Jones (No. 38)

20. Chocolate cup and saucer
Hard-paste porcelain, Meissen, Germany
1718-20
Height: 6.8cm (cup);
diameter: 12cm (saucer)
Given by Wilfred de Winton, 1918
NMW A 33223

Teacup and saucer
Hard-paste porcelain, Meissen, Germany
1717-20
Height: 4.1cm (cup);
diameter: 11.5cm (saucer)
Given by Wilfred de Winton, 1918
NMW A 33225

Teapot
Hard-paste porcelain, Meissen, Germany
About 1720
Height: 16cm; length: 18cm;
width: 10cm
Purchased, 1987
NMW A 32076

Porcelain, a hard, white and translucent ceramic body produced only in China and Japan, was widely admired in seventeenth-century Europe. The first satisfactory European porcelain was developed by Johann Friedrich Böttger (1682-1719) in Dresden in the early 1700s, and produced commercially in the Meissen factory nearby from 1710. The Museum has over a dozen pieces of the white porcelain from the factory's first decade, and three examples of the red stoneware also produced there.

At first the factory's wares were decorated with gilding or with relief ornament, such as the shells applied to this handle-less teacup, as it took several years to develop the techniques of applying coloured decoration to the creamy-white porcelain body. The inside of both teacup and saucer are coated with 'Böttger lustre', an iridescent pink glaze made from gold. Introduced in

1717, this very rare decoration was compared to mother-of-pearl and to opals.

The twisted flutes of the taller cup and its saucer are filled with 'Böttger lustre' and gilding. They are also painted with small lustre panels set in scrollwork. These scrolls are painted in enamels (coloured glass fluxes fired on to the body). During this early, experimental period, Meissen porcelain was decorated in Dresden, and these pieces may come from the workshop of the goldsmith Georg Funcke.

The teapot, in the form of a squatting bearded man on an upturned scallop shell, is a few years later. Its designer, probably the Dresden goldsmith Johann Jakob Irminger (1635-1724), took his inspiration from the *Livre des Vases* of Jacques Stella (1596-1697) published in 1667. *OF*

21. Teapot

Hard-paste porcelain, Meissen, Germany

About 1723-4

Height: 11.8cm; length: 15.5cm;
diameter: 11cm

Given by Wilfred de Winton, 1919

NMW A 32630

Teabowl and saucer

Hard-paste porcelain, Meissen, Germany

About 1722-3

Height: 4.8cm (teabowl);
diameter: 13.1 (saucer)

Given by Wilfred de Winton, 1918

NMW A 32629

Both these pieces are believed to have been painted by Johann Gregorius Höroldt (1696-1775), who joined the Meissen factory in 1720. Trained as a wallpaper painter and tapestry designer, Höroldt had learned to paint on ceramics at the Du Paquier porcelain factory in Vienna. At Meissen, he developed a range of enamel colours that are still the basic pigments used to decorate porcelain today.

The teabowl and saucer belong to a small group of early Meissen services painted with characters from the Italian *Commedia dell' Arte* (Harlequin appears on the saucer and Scaramouche and Mezzetin on the teabowl). These may be linked to Horoldt's request in August 1722 for drawings of the costumes worn in the recent Dresden carnival 'in order to paint them on services'. However he also used late seventeenth-century engravings by Jean Mariette (1660-1742) as a source.

Höroldt established an entirely new decorative vocabulary of *chinoiserie* (fantasy Chinese) scenes on porcelain. The teapot is an early example, which was inspired by engravings in late seventeenth-century travel literature. On one side three Chinese attendants accompanied by two negro servants leading a camel present a dish of fruit to an enthroned figure; on the other two further figures offer a dish and a basket to a man and woman standing behind a table covered with dishes and vessels.

Meissen established a workshop system so that all the painters under Höroldt had access to his designs and could copy them. Some of these designs, including drawings for this teapot, survive. However it is likely that the teapot, datable to 1723-4 from its KMP mark in underglaze blue, is the work of Höroldt himself. Both pieces are very rare and evidence of de Winton's connoisseurship. *OF*

22. Giovanni Antonio Canal (Canaletto)
(b. Venice, Italy 1697; d. Venice 1768)

The Bacino di San Marco, looking north
About 1730
Oil on canvas, 141.3 x 154 cm
Purchased with the assistance of
the Art Fund and other donors, 1957
NMW A 76

Canaletto was the eighteenth century's foremost painter of Venetian landscapes. His canal views were hugely influential and inspired a new genre in Italian landscape art known as *vedute*.

This is a view across the Bacino di San Marco from the eastern end of the Giudecca island. The portico of the Dogana is in the middle distance on the left and some of Venice's key landmarks stretch across the horizon. The three central buildings are the Customs House, the Basilica di San Marco and the Doge's Palace, with the Campanile towering above them.

The buildings are painted with near-photographic precision. Contemporary letters describe the artist preparing his works outdoors 'on the spot', and he is thought to have used an optical device, a *camera ottica*, to capture the detail. However his works were not simple copies of the landscape; he combined topographical detail with dramatic compositions, startling light effects and the liveliness of Venetian daily life.

The colours and technical handling are close to a group of paintings at Windsor Castle; this dates this work to around 1730. The composition also shows the influence of his formative years when he worked with his father Bernardo Canal painting theatre scenery. The couple promenading on the quayside are like actors on a stage, gesturing theatrically to the backdrop panorama. The unusual square format enhances the illusion of depth between these two points of focus, demonstrating Canaletto's consummate understanding of perspective.

By the late 1720s the connoisseur Joseph Smith was Canaletto's agent, and he introduced Canaletto's work to British visitors looking for an artistic souvenir of their Grand Tour. His popularity among British collectors endured long after his death. *AP*

23. William Hogarth
(b. London 1697; d. London 1764)

The Jones Family
1730
Oil on canvas, 72 x 91.8cm
Purchased with the assistance of the
National Heritage Memorial Fund and
the Art Fund, 1996
NMW A 3978

The Jones family is decorously arranged
in a grove with peasants making hay
behind them. Robert Jones (1706-1742)
stands holding a cane, accompanied by
his elder sister Mary, while their widowed
mother sits in subdued isolation, playing
with her pet spaniel. A younger brother
and sister, Oliver and Elizabeth, more
plainly dressed as befitted their lesser
importance in the family, sit with a
basket of flowers. Hogarth contrasts
the family's genteel poses with the
raucous behaviour of the haymakers,
two of whom are coupling on top of
one of the hayricks. Linking the two
groups is a boy dressed as a servant,
who struggles with a monkey.

Robert Jones was the owner of Fonmon
Castle in the Vale of Glamorgan, which is
represented by the castellated building in
the background. He also had a London
house in Bruton Street, Berkeley Square,
and this picture was begun in London in
March 1730 shortly before he left on a
tour of Italy that took him to Rome,
Naples and Venice. He spent about £700
on paintings on his travels.

William Hogarth began his career as
an engraver, and made his name with
graphic satires. He turned to painting
in the late 1720s and is best known for
his series pictures telling a moral tale
in several episodes, such as *The Rake's
Progress* of 1734. In 1730, however,
contemporaries noted his success with
'family pieces and conversations
consisting of many figures, done with
great spirit, a lively invention & a
universal agreeableness.' This painting,
with the Jones family interacting affably,
is a good example of the type, which has
its origins in Dutch and French group
portraiture.

This is one of the three 'conversation
piece' paintings of the early 1730s
by Hogarth in the collection. *OF*

24. Centrepiece

Silver and glass, London 1730-1

Maker's mark of Edward Feline

Height: 40.6cm; length: 58cm;
width: 49cm

Purchased with the assistance of
the Art Fund, 1995

NMW A 51194

This is oldest-known table centrepiece or epergne by an English maker. The few surviving examples from the 1730s comprise a deep dish or bowl, with attached cruets for oil and vinegar bottles and stands for casters (which contained sugar, pepper and mustard). Later on in the dinner, which generally began at about 3 o clock and lasted several hours, the cruets and casters could be removed and candle branches and dessert dishes added. This one is shown assembled but without its six casters, which are now missing.

The centrepiece reflects an important shift in dining habits around 1700 – the adoption of service à la française. Diners now sat at a table laid with a dozen or more dishes, and helped themselves from those within reach. A second course of more mixed dishes and a dessert course followed. Huge services of matching

plates and dishes became fashionable, together with tureens, baskets and centrepieces. The central bowl of this centrepiece is elaborately decorated in the French baroque manner with strap, trellis and anthemion ornament, and has on either side the arms of Williams, two crossed foxes, in relief.

From these arms, this centrepiece can be identified as the 'Old Epergne' described as an heirloom in the will of Sir John Williams of Bodelwyddan, Flintshire, in 1829. It was probably commissioned by his great-uncle Hugh Williams (?1694-1742) of Chester, who was MP for Anglesey between 1722 and 1734. It was sold at Christie's in 1920 by their descendant Sir William Willoughby Williams (1888-1932). It subsequently belonged to the American newspaper baron and collector William Randolph Hearst (1863-1951). OF

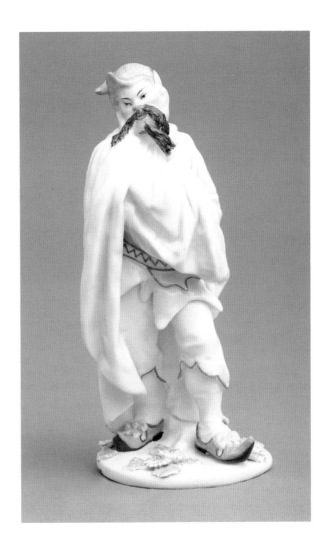

25. Chinese Mask

Soft-paste porcelain,
Chelsea, about 1754

Height: 18.1cm

Purchased with the assistance of
the Art Fund, 1972

NMW A 30061

This superbly modelled figure would have been part of a group, intended as table ornaments during the dessert course.

Chinese porcelain was collected enthusiastically during the eighteenth century and British manufacturers were desperate to unlock the secret of how to create this gleaming white, beautifully translucent ceramic. The Chelsea Porcelain Factory, established by Nicholas Sprimont (1715-1771), a Huguenot silversmith, is considered to be the first to achieve this ambition. By 1745 the factory was selling expensive, fashionable 'china' to wealthy clients, who purchased the porcelain from dealers, directly from Chelsea's showrooms or at the factory's annual auctions. A *Chinese Mask* figure is listed for sale in a Chelsea auction catalogue for 20 March 1755.

The figure was made during Chelsea's 'red anchor' period (about 1752-1756), so-called due to a variation in the factory mark. A large range of brilliantly modelled figures and figure groups were produced at Chelsea during this time. Red anchor figures covered a diverse variety of subject matter from the Italian *Commedia dell' Arte* to pastoral life, and from beggars to mythological and allegorical characters. This figure is one of several depicting Chinese subjects. Many of Chelsea's figures were created after originals by Meissen, the pre-eminent porcelain factory in Europe in the eighteenth century. However *Chinese Mask* is perhaps an original composition by Chelsea's own modeller, Joseph Willems (1716-1766), a migrant worker from what is now Belgium. His works show a familiarity with French *chinoiserie* prints after François Boucher.
RC

26. Richard Wilson
(b. Penegoes, Montgomeryshire 1713;
d. Colmendy, Flintshire 1782)

Landscape with Banditti
1754/5
Black chalk, white chalk and pencil
on laid paper, 28.2 x 40.5cm
Purchased 1954
NMW A 1884

This highly finished drawing is one of a series of sixty-eight commissioned from Wilson by William Legge, 2nd Earl of Dartmouth (1731-1801) in 1754, while both men were in Rome. Wilson has used black chalk heightened with white to create the effect of light and atmosphere. Wilson's pupil Joseph Farington (1747-1821) said that the Roman drawings 'were so excellent that it may be justly said they have all the quality of his pictures, except the colour'. The drawings were lost for over a century until 1948, when a portfolio of them was discovered at Patshull House, Staffordshire.

The subject of this work is unusual among the Dartmouth group, as it is the only known completely imaginary scene. It is strikingly similar to a painting of Wilson's from 1752, *Landscape with Banditti: The Murder*, also in the Museum's collection (see left). However this drawing is not a study for the oil painting and was produced later. The sublime landscape and inclusion of 'banditti' shows the influence on Wilson of Salvator Rosa (1615-1673) and Gaspard Poussin (1615-1675).

Wilson's sojourn in Italy shaped the rest of his career. In Rome he committed to pursuing landscape painting rather than portraiture and built up a repertoire of subjects on which he could draw back in Britain. Wilson was a founder member of the Royal Academy in 1768 and a pivotal figure in the development of landscape painting in British art. John Ruskin wrote that with his name, 'the history of sincere landscape art founded on a meditative love of nature begins in England'. *BM*

27. Richard Wilson
(b. Penegoes, Montgomeryshire 1713;
d. Colmendy, Flintshire 1782)

Pembroke Town and Castle
About 1765
Oil on canvas, 102.5 x 128.3cm
Purchased with the assistance of
the Art Fund, 1930
NMW A 64

Pembroke is seen from the west, bathed in a warm golden light across a tidal inlet of the Cleddau estuary. The composition is dominated by the early thirteenth-century round keep and jagged outline of the castle, with the Norman town clustered around the square tower of St Mary's Church beyond and to the left. Pembroke was then the largest town in south-west Wales, and the industrious figures in the foreground suggest continuity between an ancient warlike past and a more prosperous present.

Richard Wilson had spent the years 1752 to 1756 in Rome, where he was profoundly influenced by the paintings of Claude Lorrain (no. 12). Here he has applied the principles of the idealised classical landscape to a real place, which he had visited and drawn. He has introduced a framing cliff on the left, and raised the height of the river bank below the castle to have the walls reflected in the water below.

The 1750s saw an increasing interest in Britain in the history and culture of ancient Wales, and Wilson responded by painting several Welsh subjects. Some of these pictures were commissioned by Welshmen active in this mid-eighteenth century Celtic Revival. This painting is one of several that may have been commissioned by William Vaughan (1707-1775), first president of the Cymmrodorion.

Sometimes described as 'the father of English landscape painting', Wilson had a profound influence on both Turner and Constable. As the first artist of European stature from Wales, he was seen as central to the art collections of the National Museum. This painting, acquired for £1,900 in 1930, was perhaps the Museum's most important purchase of the inter-war period. *OF*

28. Vase

Marble, 1st century BC, and about 1770
Height: 172cm; diameter: 119.5cm
Purchased with the assistance of
the Art Fund, 1976
NMW A 14

The central cylinder of the vase is a Roman well-head or altar, carved in relief with the marriage of Paris, son of King Priam of Troy, to Helen of Sparta, attended by Eros, Aphrodite and three of the muses. It was first recorded at Pozzuoli, near Naples. In about 1769 it was bought from the Carrafa collection in Naples by one of the best-known figures of the British community in eighteenth-century Rome, the painter, dealer and banker Thomas Jenkins (1722-1798). Jenkins had it mounted as a vase, by the addition of the vine leaf frieze and lip above, and the cup with Satyr's heads, stem and base below.

Classical sculpture was keenly collected by British visitors to Italy, who expected their purchases to be restored to what was believed to be their original appearance. The huge marble vessels known after their owners as the Borghese and Medici vases were particularly admired. Purchasers of Roman sculpture included Sir Watkin Williams-Wynn (see no. 29) and Thomas Mansel Talbot (1747-1813) of Penrice, Glamorgan. In 1774 Jenkins told Charles Townley (1737-1805), the most erudite and committed collector of the period, that this piece 'turns out so fine that I believe it will be sold for £500. In short it is the Very first Vase in the World.' He had an account of its iconography published and in 1775 he sold it to Townley's friend James Hugh Smith Barry (1746-1801). Barry was one of Jenkins's most extravagant clients, who assembled a collection of forty classical sculptures during the 1770s, as well as paintings and other antiquities for his family home, Marbury Hall, Cheshire. *OF*

29. Pompeo Batoni

(b. Lucca, Italy 1708; d. Rome 1787)

Sir Watkin Williams-Wynn, Thomas Apperley and Captain Edward Hamilton

1768-72

Oil on canvas, 289 x 196cm

Purchased, 1947

NMW A 78

Sir Watkin Williams-Wynn (1749-1789), 4th baronet, is the red-haired figure on the left. He was nineteen when he commissioned this portrait in Rome in 1768 during a six-month tour of Italy. He had himself painted with two of his travelling companions, and this great picture celebrates their shared love of painting, represented by the allegorical sculpture in the background, and of music and poetry. Sir Watkin grasps a crayon-holder and his own drawing after a Raphael fresco in the Vatican. Edward Hamilton holds a flute, and gestures towards Thomas Apperley (1734-1819) of Plas Grono, Denbighshire, who reads out a poem by Dante.

Sir Watkin inherited the vast Wynnstay estate in north Wales while still a baby and was the richest Welshman of his day. His father had been a national figure and one of Robert Walpole's most vocal opponents in the House of Commons. The son was much more interested in the

arts. While making the Grand Tour in 1768-9, he bought paintings and classical antiquities, and also commissioned new works.

Pompeo Batoni had made his name in Rome with altarpieces and history paintings, but from the 1750s he painted portraits of British visitors to Italy. These were elaborately composed and full of special effects, such as the lively interplay here between the figures and the rich naturalism of their dress. He took four years to complete this picture, which is perhaps his masterpiece. It was sent by sea from Livorno to London, where it was hung in Sir Watkin's town house in St James's Square.

The Williams-Wynn family sold the painting in 1947. During that period of post-war austerity Batoni's work was profoundly unfashionable, and this picture was bought by the Museum for just £230. *OF*

30. Toilet service

Silver gilt, glass and velvet,
London 1768-9

Maker's mark of Thomas Heming,
(snuffer tray marked Emick Romer)

Height: 70.5cm (mirror)

Purchased with the assistance of
the Art Fund, 1964

NMW A 50386-50414

Grand ladies often received friends in their dressing rooms as they completed their 'toilet'. From the 1660s silver toilet services were a symbol of rank and high status, often displayed on dressing tables with rich lace covers.

By the mid-eighteenth century, such services were becoming less common. This one was ordered by Sir Watkin Williams-Wynn's mother for her new daughter-in-law, Lady Henrietta Somerset (1748-1769), a daughter of the 4th Duke of Beaufort (see left). It was a breathtaking statement of social ambition on her part. It was supplied by the royal goldsmith Thomas Heming in 1768-9 and eighteen pieces are almost identical to those in a service he had made two years earlier for King George III's sister Princess Caroline Matilda when she married the King of Denmark. In 1772 Queen Charlotte ordered a third service of this design from him.

It comprises a mirror, two candlesticks, a ewer and dish, a glove tray, two chap bowls (the tureen-like vessels) for cosmetics, brushes, whisks, scent bottles and flasks and caskets for ribbons, patches, and laces. It is decorated with naturalistic flowering sprays and shells in the late rococo manner. The ewer, with its symbols of water, is after a design by the celebrated French silversmith Thomas Germain (1673-1748), while the figure-candlesticks are adapted from a French baroque prototype of the late seventeenth century.

Henrietta died three months after her wedding, but the service was used by Sir Watkin's second wife Charlotte (see no. 32). It remained in the Williams-Wynn family until 1964. *OF*

31. Organ

Pine, limewood, mahogany, oak, plaster, bronze, carved, painted and gilded; pipemetal, leather, iron, ivory

Case designed by Robert Adam (1728-1792) and made by Robert Ansell, London, 1773-4

Organ made by John Snetzler (1710-1785), London, 1774-5

Height: 411.4cm; width: 323cm; depth: 104.8cm

Purchased with the assistance of the National Heritage Memorial Fund and the Art Fund, 1995

NMW A 51193

This organ was made for Wynn House in St James's Square, Sir Watkin Williams-Wynn's London house. It formed part of the complex neo-classical interiors Robert Adam created there. Sir Watkin was a leading amateur musician of the day, and the organ's central medallion bears a portrait of George Frederick Handel, his favourite composer. The draped female figures are two of the nine muses – Euterpe, the muse of music and lyric poetry with a pipe, and Terpsichore, the muse of dancing and song with a lyre. The doors below open sideways to reveal the two keyboards or manuals.

The case was made in the workshop of Robert Ansell, who also supplied the mirrors, the picture frames and some architectural furniture for Wynn House. The organ itself is the work of the Swiss-born John Snetzler, the leading London builder of his day, who was famous for the bright clear sound of his instruments. He was paid £250 plus a £4 a year retainer for tuning.

The organ was made for the ground-floor music room. It occupied the centre of the wall opposite the fireplace, which was flanked by the paintings *St Cecilia* by Sir Joshua Reynolds and *Orpheus* by Nathaniel Dance, symbolising sacred and profane music.

Sir Watkin Williams-Wynn moved into his house in 1775, and celebrated with a musical breakfast. The organ was enlarged in 1864 by the firm of Gray and Davison and moved to Wynnstay, the family's Denbighshire home, where it remained until 1995. *OF*

32. Sir Joshua Reynolds
(b. Plympton, Devon 1723;
d. London 1792)

**Lady Charlotte Williams-Wynn and
her three eldest children**
About 1778
Oil on canvas, 159.4 x 215.7cm
Purchased with the assistance of the
Heritage Lottery Fund and of
the Art Fund, 1998
NMW A 12964

Charlotte Grenville (1754-1830) became
Sir Watkin Williams-Wynn's second wife
in December 1771. She came from a
great political family. Her father George
Grenville (1712-1770) was Prime
Minister in 1763-5; after his death her
uncle, Earl Temple, became her guardian.
Another uncle, by marriage, was the
statesman William Pitt the Elder.
She had seven children, and is probably
painted here with the three elder ones –
Watkin, Marie Catherine (who died in
1778) and Charles. She is dressed in what
was then known as Turkish fashion, in a
gown with a plunging v-shaped neckline
and a scarf wound turban-like in her hair,
an effect intensified by the large cushion
and carpet. Her pose, reclining with a
book, may derive from the pastel
portraits of ladies in Turkish dress by the
Swiss Jean-Étienne Liotard (1702-1789),

who was in England in 1772-6 and
exhibited at the Royal Academy in
1773-4.

Reynolds was the most innovative
portrait painter of the mid-eighteenth
century, and as the first President of the
Royal Academy from 1768, the most
famous artist of the day. He painted four
whole-length portraits of members of the
Williams-Wynn family. This one is an
example of his 'grand manner', where the
composition is derived from Italian High
Renaissance Art of the sixteenth century
– in this case paintings of The Rest on the
Flight into Egypt. The richness of colour
recalls Titian and the children's pose is
taken from his *Vendramin Family*
(National Gallery, London). *OF*

33. William Parry
(b. London 1743; d. London 1791)

John Parry

About 1770

Oil on canvas, 84.8 x 73.9cm

Purchased, 1996

NMW A 3979

Born near Nefyn in Caernarvonshire, and blind from birth, John Parry (about 1710-1782) was a celebrated musician and harpist to the Williams-Wynn family of Wynnstay. He published three pioneering collections of music – *Ancient British Harmony* (1742), *A Collection of Welsh, English and Scottish Airs* (1761) and *British Harmony* (1781) – and was perhaps the greatest Welsh musician of the eighteenth century. He claimed that his music was of druidical origin, and the triple harp he played was later adopted as the national instrument of Wales. The composer Handel admired him, and his 'ravishing blind harmony' with 'tunes enough to choke you' inspired the poet Thomas Gray to finish writing *The Bard* in 1757 (see no. 37).

This sensitive portrait of 'Blind Parry' was painted by his elder son, William, who had completed his training as an artist by working as a studio assistant to Reynolds in 1765-8. It probably dates from 1770, when William was working for his father's patron, Sir Watkin Williams-Wynn (see no. 29), as he also painted another version which originally hung at Wynnstay with Anton Mengs's portrait of Richard Wilson. Later that year William Parry left for Italy, where he worked and studied for four years, funded by Sir Watkin Williams-Wynn. On his return he worked both in London and Wales painting portraits and small conversation pieces. The latter include his portrait of Omai, the Polynesian brought to England by Captain Cook, with Sir Joseph Banks and the Swedish botanist Daniel Solander, which later belonged to his friends and patrons the Vaughan family of Nannau, Merioneth (see no. 50). *OF*

34. Johann Zoffany
(b. Frankfurt-am-Main, Germany 1733;
d. London 1810)

**Henry Knight of Tythegston
with his three children**
About 1770

Oil on canvas, 240.5 x 149cm

Purchased with funds bequeathed by
Miss June Tiley and with the assistance
of the Heritage Lottery Fund and the
Art Fund, 1999

NMW A 13702

The painting shows Henry Knight (1739-
1772) surrounded by his three children
Henry (born 1763), Robert (born 1764)
and Ethelreda (born 1767). His wife
Catherine Lynch had left him and was
living with her lover in London. The
Knights divorced, which was then a
socially disastrous process requiring
a private Act of Parliament, in 1771.
Faced with this crisis, Henry resigned his
commission in the army. In the picture he
thrusts his spontoon, a short pike carried
by infantry officers, point first into the
sand. Robert holds his sword, while the
younger Henry plays with a helmet of
the 15th Light Dragoons (this may be
a studio prop, chosen for its classical
appearance, as Henry had no known
association with this regiment).

Henry Knight was the squire of
Tythegston, near Porthcawl, and this
portrait is a surprisingly large and
expensive image for a Glamorgan gentry
family of moderate wealth. It was
probably an assertion of his new role, as
a single parent. He had a keen interest in
the arts, and took drawing lessons and
collected pictures, including works by
Rubens and Jacob Ruisdael.

Zoffany had settled in London in 1760,
where he quickly made a name for
himself with conversation piece portraits
of family groups. Established as Queen
Charlotte's favourite painter, he was a
founder member of the Royal Academy
in 1768. His success was based on his
ability to catch a likeness and his
astonishingly accurate treatment of
textiles and dress. Here the placing of
the older son in the tree produces a
harmoniously triangular composition,
and gives the figures equal prominence.
OF

35. Thomas Gainsborough
(b. Sudbury, Suffolk 1727;
d. London 1788)

**Rocky Wooded Landscape with
Rustic Lovers**
1771-4
Oil and canvas, 124.2 x 149.3cm
Accepted by H.M. Government in lieu
of inheritance tax, 2001
NMW A 22780

This picture is one of Gainsborough's most beautiful landscapes, painted during his final years in Bath. It combines bucolic cattle by a watering place, idyllic pastoral lovers and a distant golden landscape to evoke a feeling of nostalgia for an imaginary rural past. The handling of paint is bold, with slabs of white, yellow and pink impasto in the sky. Gainsborough sometimes said that while portraiture was his profession, landscape painting was his pleasure. By 1770 his landscapes are carefully contrived, and this composition borrows from Claude (no. 12) and Rubens.

This picture was probably painted at Shockerwick Manor, home of the Bath carrier Walter Wiltshire (c. 1719-1799). Gainsborough was a frequent visitor there and he used Wiltshire's regular 'flying waggon' service to transport his paintings to London. He gave Wiltshire this and *The Harvest Waggon* when he left Bath for London in 1774. The latter

dates from 1767, and *Rocky Wooded Landscape* appears to have been painted as a pendant to it, either in 1771 or shortly before he left for London. The pictures stayed together until 1946, when *The Harvest Waggon* was acquired by the Barber Institute, Birmingham, and *Rocky Wooded Landscap* was bought by William Berry, Viscount Camrose (1879-1956). Born in Merthyr Tydfil, Berry and his brother Gomer built up a media empire that included the *Sunday Times*, the *Financial Times*, regional titles and from 1927 the *Daily Telegraph*.

This is the most significant of several Gainsborough works in the collection, which include a smaller landscape of 1783 bequeathed by Gwendoline Davies, a portrait of Thomas Pennant (no. 36) and *Rocky Landscape with Hagar and Ishmael*, Gainsborough's only biblical painting, acquired by Sir Watkin Williams-Wynn. *OF*

36. Thomas Gainsborough
(b. Sudbury, Suffolk 1727;
d. London 1788)

Thomas Pennant
1776
Oil and canvas, 95 x 74cm
Purchased, 1953
NMW A 97

The hilly landscape behind Thomas
Pennant (1726-1798) suggests his native
Wales, the book by his side that he is
a gentleman scholar. The squire of
Downing, near Holywell in Flintshire,
Pennant was a traveller, naturalist and
antiquarian. By 1776 he was already well
known as the author of *British Zoology*
(1766) and *Genera of Birds* (1773).
These were followed by *History of
Quadrupeds* (1781) and *Arctic Zoology*
(1785). He was perhaps the eighteenth
century's most distinguished British
zoologist.

In 1769 Pennant undertook a tour of
Scotland, chiefly of the highlands, a
region then little known by outsiders but
of interest for its natural history. Several
tours throughout Wales followed in the

early 1770s with his Welsh-speaking
friend and companion the Reverend John
Lloyd of Caerwys. These were published
in three volumes as *Tours in Wales*
(1778-83). They explored the topography
and history of Wales in unprecedented
detail, and inspired many other such
guides over the next half-century. He
was accompanied on his travels by his
draughtsman Moses Griffith (1747-
1819), whose many watercolours in the
collection are a fascinating window on
eighteenth-century Wales.

Thomas Gainsborough had moved from
Bath to London in 1774, where he soon
rivalled Reynolds as a fashionable
portraitist. This picture shows his relaxed
informality and characteristic loose
feathery brushwork. *OF*

37. Thomas Jones
(b. Trefonnen, Radnorshire 1742;
d. Pencerrig, Radnorshire 1803)

The Bard
1774
Oil on canvas, 114.5 x 168cm
Purchased, 1965
NMW A 85

This is an illustration of Thomas Gray's poem of the same name, published in 1757. This was one of the principal literary texts in English to inspire the mid-eighteenth century Celtic revival. It recounts the legendary tale of Edward I's massacre of the Welsh bards, and the curse of the last survivor who threw himself to his death into the river Conwy below as the English king's army approaches through the mountains.

The circle of standing stones was inspired by Stonehenge, which Jones had visited in 1769. Unaware that it belonged to a yet more ancient past, he believed this 'Stupendous Monument of Antiquity' to be Druidic. By introducing it here, he merges the image of the mediaeval bard with that of the Celtic druids, also massacred by the Romans. Particularly in Wales, the bard-druid then became a patriotic symbol of British resistance to Continental tyranny.

The second son of a Radnorshire gentry family, Thomas Jones had been a pupil in Richard Wilson's studio in 1763-5. This composition owes something to Wilson's 'history' paintings as well as to the seventeenth-century masters Gaspard Dughet and Salvator Rosa, whom Wilson greatly admired. Jones described it in his *Memoirs* as one of his best paintings. This opinion was shared by the *Middlesex Journal*, which described it as 'finely romantic … a most capital piece' when it was exhibited at the Society of Artists in 1774. *OF*

38. Thomas Jones
(b. Trefonnen, Radnorshire 1742;
d. Pencerrig, Radnorshire 1803)

Buildings in Naples
1782
Oil on paper, 14.2 x 21.6cm
Purchased, 1954
NMW A 89

This compelling view was painted from the roof terrace of the artist's lodgings opposite the Dogana del Sale in Naples. It shows a rooftop view of the city, but the painting is dominated by the humble Neapolitan house opposite – the real subject of this work. Jones has captured in minute detail the texture of the crumbling wall, the half-shuttered windows and doorway, all bathed in sunlight.

This is one of a number of oil sketches that surfaced on the art market in 1954 and completely changed Jones's reputation. The sketches are characterized by their humble subjects and compositional cropping, which give them a startlingly modern appearance. These works show the artist painting his daily surroundings. They were not for exhibition or sale, but personal works, made for his own enjoyment. Today they are prized as some of the most innovative pictures of their time.

Jones had been a pupil in the studio of Richard Wilson. Here he learnt the 'grand' style of landscape composition, which he adopted in his own larger landscape paintings. Like his teacher Wilson, Jones was drawn to Italy and set off in October 1776. He wrote that it was 'a favourite project that had been in agitation for some Years, and on which my heart was fixed'. He stayed in Rome and Naples, returning home in 1783. The Museum's collection also has a sketchbook full of meticulous pencil studies from his time in Italy. While he made a living from selling large, carefully composed landscape canvases, it is the small oil studies that are Thomas Jones's best-known artistic legacy. *BM*

39. Thomas Rowlandson
(b. London 1756; d. London 1827)

Skaters on the Serpentine
1784
Pen and ink, watercolour and pencil on paper, 42.6 x 72.7cm
Purchased, 1976
NMW A 1737

A crowd gathers on a winter's day at the Serpentine Lake in Hyde Park, London. In the middle distance, half-hidden by the crowd, skaters, some arm in arm, glide around the lake. People have set up temporary stalls, offering drinks or skate hire, others are out begging. In the distance the now destroyed Cheesecake House can be seen, a refreshment lodge for visitors to the park.

However, this is not just an observation of humanity and life. Rowlandson also uses pale washes to convey the atmosphere of a cold, frosty day. The air is misty, the trees are bare and a low sun casts long shadows. This work was first exhibited at the Royal Academy in 1784 titled *The Serpentine River*.

Rowlandson was one of the foremost draughtsmen of his generation and a celebrated social satirist. He entered the Royal Academy Schools in 1772 and developed a unique drawing style using vigorous ink lines and watercolour washes. He was much influenced by the artist and satirist William Hogarth (1697-1764). London provided Rowlandson with a never-ending variety of people to observe, which he captured with great wit and insight. He also travelled widely in Britain and Europe. He toured Wales with the author Henry Wigstead (1760-1800) in 1797. The popularity of his work was enhanced by his success as a printmaker. The Museum has a version of the comic print *An Artist travelling in Wales* (see left) from the *Tour of Dr Syntax in Search of the Picturesque* (1799). *BM*

40. Pieces from a dessert service

Soft-paste porcelain, Derby, 1787

Various sizes, the centre dish height: 8.3cm; length: 32cm; width: 25.4cm

Purchased, 1991, 1998, and 2006; given by Nicholas S. Harris, 1996

NMW A 30223, 30226, 32653, 33791, 38159

This service was commissioned from the Derby factory early in 1787 by the Cardiganshire landowner Thomas Johnes (1748-1816). Comprising thirty-seven pieces and costing £63, it was the most expensive recorded dessert service produced at Derby in the late eighteenth century. Each piece was decorated with a different view of Johnes's gothic mansion at Hafod and the picturesque landscape he was creating around it. The decorator was probably copying views by Thomas Jones, who was sketching at Hafod in the autumn of 1786. They may indeed have been the 'large portfolio, full of paintings (on paper) of a variety of views round' Hafod by Jones that Johnes is recorded as showing to the travel writer William Gilpin (1724-1804).

Johnes had married his cousin Jane Johnes (d. 1833) in 1783, and they went to live at Hafoduchtryd, Cardiganshire. Under the influence of Richard Payne Knight (1751-1824), another cousin, Johnes 'improved' his remote and barren estate according to 'picturesque' principles. This involved a massive programme of land improvement, and the planting of some five million trees between 1784 and 1811. The new house at Hafod was built from the designs of Thomas Baldwin of Bath. The house, with its great library and irreplaceable collections of Welsh manuscripts, was destroyed by fire in 1807, and rebuilt, again by Baldwin.

The completed service was delivered to Johnes in March 1788. It was subsequently dispersed and sixteen pieces are now in the Museum's collection. Shown here are the large centre dish (South Front, Hafod), a square dish (in Maen Arthur), an oval dish (Cold Bath), a heart-shaped dish (the Menagerie) and a plate (from the Menagerie). *OF*

41. Joseph Mallord William Turner
(b. London 1775; d. London 1851)

Transept of Ewenny Priory, Glamorganshire
About 1797
Watercolour and pencil with scraping-out and stopping out on paper, 40.1 x 55.7cm
Bequeathed by James Pyke Thompson, 1898
NMW A 1734

Turner has captured a powerful, atmospheric view of the south transept of Ewenny Priory in the Vale of Glamorgan. This exhibition watercolour is based on a drawing in a sketchbook made while Turner was touring south Wales in 1795 (Tate). Turner visited Wales five times in eight years during the 1790s, gathering material for future paintings and watercolours.

The priory church of St Michael, Ewenny was founded by William de Londres, Lord of Ogmore. It was built in about 1115-20 as a Benedictine foundation for a prior and ten to fifteen monks. The effigy of a knight on the tomb to the right of the work is probably that of Sir Paganus de Turberville of Coity, a twelfth-century benefactor of the Priory.

When exhibited at the Royal Academy in 1797, this highly finished work marked Turner out as a pioneer of painting in watercolour and an innovator of the medium. One contemporary critic wrote, 'In point of colour and effect this is one of the grandest Drawings we have ever seen; and equal to the best Pictures of Rembrandt.' The bold use of light and the exaggerated perspective shows the influence of both Rembrandt (1606-1669) and Giovanni Battista Piranesi (1720-1778). The way Turner manipulated the watercolour to create luminous effects may also show the influence of the Swiss artist Abraham-Louis-Rodolphe Ducros (1748-1810). Turner would have had the opportunity to see work by all these artists in the collection of the antiquarian and artist Richard Colt Hoare (1758-1838) at Stourhead, Wiltshire, while there in 1795.
BM

Nineteenth-century art

The art collection formed by the Cardiff Museum from the 1880s and later transferred to the National Museum was dominated by recent British and French paintings and Welsh ceramics. The latter has remained an important focus, and many bequests and gifts have given the Museum an unequalled collection, which is especially rich in the fine porcelains of Swansea and Nantgarw.

British nineteenth-century painting in the collection ranges from works by Constable, Turner and Samuel Palmer through the Pre-Raphaelites to Whistler and British followers of Impressionism. The Merthyr-born painter Penry Williams (1802-1885), who settled in Rome in 1828, is represented by over three hundred paintings and drawings. Mid-Victorian artists who worked in Wales include David Cox, John Brett and William Dyce. The many portraits in the collection include some by largely self-taught Welsh artists such as Hugh Hughes and William Roos.

The collection is especially rich in nineteenth-century British sculpture. One focus is John Gibson (1790-1866), who also trained and worked in Rome. Another is the British 'New Sculpture' movement of the 1880s and 1890s. One of its younger members, Sir William Goscombe John (1860-1952), gave many pieces by sculptors he admired, such as Alfred Gilbert, as well as much of his own work. He was also an important donor of Victorian drawings.

The French painting and sculpture from the 1840s to the early 1900s are outstanding, and justly famous. The Menelaus collection included several pictures by modern French, German and Belgian artists, and more were added through James Pyke Thompson; but the great bequests made by Gwendoline and Margaret Davies are essentially a personal exploration of the progressive in French art from Corot to Cézanne. The artists that the sisters enjoyed, especially Daumier, Millet, Carrière and Monet, are represented by many works. As well as being major patrons of Rodin, the sisters were among the first British collectors to buy Impressionist and Post-Impressionist art.

Right: detail from *La Parisienne* by Auguste Renoir (No. 77)

42. Jug

Pearlware, Cambrian Pottery, Swansea, about 1800-05

Enamelled and gilded by Thomas Pardoe (1770-1823)

Height: 24.5cm

Given by F. E. Andrews, 1922

NMW A 30556

Mug

Pearlware, Cambrian Pottery, Swansea, 1803-06

Enamelled by William Weston Young (1776-1847)

Gilded by Thomas Pardoe (1770-1823)

Height: 15.5cm

Given by W. J. Grant-Davidson, 1994

NMW A 32245

Mug

Pearlware, Cambrian Pottery, Swansea, about 1805

Enamelled and gilded by Thomas Pardoe (1770-1823)

Height: 15.9cm

Given by the Friends of Amgueddfa Cymru – National Museum Wales, 1956

NMW A 30395

The tiger painted on the jug copies an engraving in the first volume of George Shaw's *General Zoology*, published in 1800. The landscape with oak and palm trees is the product of the imagination of Thomas Pardoe, chief painter at the Cambrian Pottery from about 1795 to 1809. The jug illustrates just one facet of Pardoe's extensive repertoire, which embraced landscapes and figures, Chinese styles, birds, shells and flowers. Pardoe left the Cambrian Pottery in 1809 to run his own business in Bristol, decorating ceramics, designing painted windows and instructing women in the art of painting china and velvet. From 1821 he spent his last years painting porcelain at Nantgarw.

Inscribed 'Druid' in the hand of William Weston Young, the first mug is a unique depiction of this subject but relates to a number of mugs painted with the Welsh Bard. Young worked for the Cambrian Pottery proprietor Lewis Weston Dillwyn

(1778-1855) as a scientific illustrator and pottery painter (from 1803 to 1806). His multifarious career included, among other things, working as a wreck-raiser and land surveyor.

The portrait of Horatio Nelson (1758-1805) on the second mug derives from mezzotints after portraits by Lemuel Francis Abbott (c. 1760-1802) but may also owe something to Pardoe's own memory of Nelson, who visited the Cambrian Pottery in 1802.

The Cambrian Pottery was at its creative peak under the leadership of Lewis Weston Dillwyn and his partner, the Philadelphia businessman George Haynes (1745-1830). Founded in 1764, the Pottery was expanded and re-equipped after Haynes bought into it in about 1789, and maintained its ambitious standards after Dillwyn's American father acquired it in 1802. *AR*

43. Pieces from a dessert service

Soft-paste porcelain

Swansea, about 1816-20

Various sizes, the ice-cream pail height:
19.6cm; width: 24.7 cm;
diameter: 19.8cm

Purchased with the assistance of the
Art Fund, 1998

NMW A 33708-33749

Porcelain dessert services, used only
for the final, dessert course of a dinner,
had long been elaborately designed and
decorated symbols of status. This is one
of the finest to be produced in Britain
during the early nineteenth century, and
helps explain why the porcelains made in
Swansea between 1815 and 1817 were
highly valued at the time, and have been
ever since. It originally comprised about
fifty pieces – forty-two of which are now
in the Museum's collection.

All the pieces are made of a porcelain
body comprising china clay, china stone,
bone ash and ball clay, which was in use
between the autumn of 1816 and the
summer of 1817. This has a pale greenish
translucency, and a lustrous glaze. Each
piece is painted with one or more garden
flowers set amid grasses within a border
of hatched and shaded gilding.

The proprietor of the Cambrian Pottery
in Swansea, Lewis Weston Dillwyn had
embarked on porcelain manufacture in
the autumn of 1814, recruiting William
Billingsley and Samuel Walker from the
small Nantgarw China Works near
Cardiff. Dillwyn planned to make very
high quality wares for a socially select
market. Swansea porcelain was available
only from the factory and from the
leading London china dealers. Some
pieces, including this service, were
decorated not at the factory but by
an independent decorating business,
probably in London.

The service is first listed in an inventory
at Burghley House, near Stamford, in
1853, and was probably acquired by
Brownlow Cecil, 2nd Marquess of
Exeter (1795-1867) soon after he came
of age in 1816. It remained at Burghley
until 1959. *OF*

44. Dessert plate

Soft-paste porcelain

Swansea, 1816-17

Diameter: 21.7cm

Enamelled and gilded by Thomas Baxter junior (1782-1821)

Given by the Friends of Amgueddfa Cymru – National Museum Wales, 1992

NMW A 31074

Dessert plate

Soft-paste porcelain

Swansea, 1816-18

Diameter: 21.5cm

Enamelled and gilded by Thomas Baxter junior (1782-1821)

Accepted in lieu of inheritance tax by H.M. Government, 2006

NMW A 38267

The first plate is painted in Thomas Baxter's characteristic soft stipple technique with marigolds, anemones and convolvulus set against a distant landscape with a lake and summer house. Never used on porcelain before, this type of composition was probably inspired by similar depictions of flowers in Robert Thornton's *Temple of Flora* of 1799-1807.

The plate is from a magnificent dessert service painted by Baxter for the Swansea factory's proprietor, Lewis Weston Dillwyn. The contract of September 1817 in which Dillwyn transferred the lease of the Swansea works to his erstwhile partners Timothy and John Bevington states 'that the china dessert service painted with Garden Scenery by Mr. Baxter, shall be the property of L. W. Dillwyn'. With the exception of two plates, the service remains intact in a private collection.

The shells on a marble shelf painted on the second plate are probably based on observation of real specimens. They do not appear in published sources like Lewis Weston Dillwyn's own *Descriptive Catalogue of Recent Shells* (1817). If, however, they were part of Dillwyn's personal collection, they cannot be identified with any of the surviving specimens in the Museum's Dillwyn collection.

Baxter worked in Swansea from 1816 to 1818, probably on a freelance basis as he also advertised himself as a miniature painter and drawing master and published engravings of local views in his own name. Trained in London under Henry Fuseli at the Royal Academy Schools and in his father's decorating workshop, he was arguably the finest British porcelain painter of his time. *AR*

45. Cream tureen

Soft-paste porcelain

Swansea, about 1817

Height: 18.5cm; diameter: 14.5cm

Purchased, 1992

NMW A 31079

Cabinet cup and saucer

Soft-paste porcelain

Nantgarw, 1818-20

Height: 10cm (cup);
diameter: 15cm (saucer)

Purchased, 1995

NMW A 32623

These two pieces demonstrate how the porcelains made at Swansea and Nantgarw were often based on French prototypes. The small tureen copies a shape made at several porcelain factories in Paris during the early nineteenth century. A similar tureen was also produced by the Spode factory where it was described as a 'French cream bowl on three claws'. The Nantgarw cup is a copy of the Sèvres *tasse Jasmin*, another shape also made in several Paris factories.

The tureen is made of a soapstone porcelain developed at Swansea in 1817. The body is painted with a band of garden flowers including morning glory, pink roses, a purple and yellow tulip and bluebells, and the upper side of the drum base with pink roses and blue and purple convolvulus. The Swansea factory was celebrated for the quality of its flower painting, and these are probably the

work of David Evans, who was later employed at Grainger's in Worcester and in Staffordshire.

The Nantgarw cup is an expensive personalised object, decorated, like much Nantgarw porcelain, outside the factory. It bears the monogram 'JW' in shaded monochrome reserved on an oblong gilt panel, within swags of brightly coloured flowers suspended from a central ring and supported on either side by a dove in flight. The unusual dry blue ground and diaper gilding are again copied from contemporary Paris porcelain. It is marked in gilt script 'Welsh Porcelain / Asser', indicating that it was sold by the firm of Henry Asser and Co, one of the principal London china dealers. The business moved to 406 Strand in 1808, and in 1822 to the newly built Burlington Arcade. *OF*

46. Dish
Soft-paste porcelain
Nantgarw, 1821-1823
Enamelled and gilded by Thomas Pardoe
(1770-1823)
Length: 30.1cm
Purchased, 1893
NMW A 31421

Plate
Soft-paste porcelain
Nantgarw, 1821-1823
Enamelled and gilded by Thomas Pardoe
(1770-1823)
Diameter: 21.5cm
Given by Wilfred de Winton, 1918
NMW A 30468

The dish shows William Edwards's bridge over the River Taff at Pontypridd, with the river in spate. The high arch is about five miles from Nantgarw and the view is most likely based on direct observation by Pardoe. The bridge has pierced haunches to reduce its weight, and when completed in 1756 it was the world's longest single-span bridge. It quickly became one of the sights of south Wales. Like the great majority of porcelain decorated at Nantgarw, the dish was doubtless decorated for a local customer. Although the initials appear to read 'JW' rather than 'TW', there is evidence that they are those of Thomas Williams (Gwilym Morgannwg, 1778-1835), bardic poet and innkeeper.

The plate is among the most sophisticated of Pardoe's work at Nantgarw. The *caillouté* ('pebbled') gilding on the rim and the composition of two pheasants perched on a branch

are modelled on luxurious French porcelain produced at Vincennes and Sèvres in the 1750s and 1760s. The birds follow a watercolour by Pardoe in a sketchbook in the Museum's collection. Pardoe's painting on Nantgarw porcelain mostly relies on his stock repertoire or is cursorily painted for sale to the local market, suggesting that this fine plate could have been a special commission.

William Billingsley (1758-1828), the idealistic and perennially impecunious moving spirit behind the loss-making Nantgarw porcelain enterprise, left the china works abruptly in 1820. Left to make the best of a perilous situation, Billingsley's financial backer William Weston Young turned to Pardoe, his former colleague at the Cambrian Pottery. Pardoe decorated the remaining stock for sale locally until his death at Nantgarw in 1823. *AR*

47. Vase

Silver, London 1815-16

Maker's mark of Paul Storr

Height: 61cm; length: 95.2cm; width: 66cm

Given by the British Coal Corporation, 1997

NMW A 51210

This monumental vase weighs nearly 44 kilos (1,414 troy ounces) and has a capacity of 63.5 litres (14 gallons). The neo-classical form is based on that of an ancient vase in the Villa Albani in Rome, and may have been designed by the architect Charles Heathcote Tatham (1772-1842), who described 'Massiveness' as 'the principal characteristic of good Plate.' It was made in the workshop of Paul Storr for the royal goldsmiths Rundell, Bridge and Rundell.

It was presented by the freeholders of Denbighshire to Sir Watkin Williams-Wynn, 5th baronet, who was their Member of Parliament, to commemorate his services during the Revolutionary and Napoleonic Wars. These comprised leading his own regiment of volunteer cavalry, the Ancient British Light Dragoons, to Ireland, where it took a bloody part in the suppression of the Rebellion of 1798, and accompanying the Denbighshire Militia to Bordeaux in 1814. The cost, nearly £1,400, was raised by public subscription. The vase was presented to Sir Watkin at a public dinner at the County Hall in Ruthin on 21 May 1816. As well as dedicatory inscriptions in Latin and English, the vase is engraved with an englyn (a classic Welsh verse form) by the Denbighshire tailor and poet Robert Davies (1769-1835):

Y. FAIL. ARIAN. AM. FILWRIO. RODDWYD / I. RADDOL. FWYN. CYMRO. / SIR. WATKIN. BRIGIN. EIN. BRO / IW. CYFARCH. AI. HIR. COFIO / CRYM. GWIR. RAID. YN. BLAID. DDYDD. BLIN. IR. CORON / FUR. CWROL. SIR. WATKIN / MARCHOG. PURAF. FLAENAF. LIN / IW. FRO. ANWYL. AI. FRENHIN

Sold in 1946 for £650, the vase was given to the National Coal Board by A. F. Mitchell-Hedges (1882-1959), and used as the coal industry's national first aid competition trophy between 1948 and 1994. *OF*

48. Ice-cream vase

Hard-paste porcelain

Sèvres, France, 1818-20

Gilt-bronze mount

Height: 33.6cm; width: 27.6cm; diameter: 22.7cm

Purchased, 1988

NMW A 30143

This ice-cream vase was made as part of a ninety-five piece dessert service, manufactured in the French state porcelain factory at Sèvres, just outside Paris, and painted with South American birds. Porcelain painters usually copied their subjects from engravings, but for this service Sèvres recruited Pauline Knip (1781-1855), the best ornithological artist in Paris.

Sèvres had become the most creative porcelain factory in Europe under its director Alexandre Brongniart (1770-1847), who was himself a chemist, mineralogist and zoologist. This service reflects his scientific interests. Each piece is painted with a bird within a gilded border of feathers and South American plants. The birds are placed on supports of gilding, comprising the plants that form their food or habitat. Humming birds and other symbols of sweetness were used on the sugar bowls, while water or marsh birds were chosen for the ice-cream pails.

Pauline Knip insisted on working at home rather than in the factory, and porcelain with delicate unfired enamel painting had to be sent back and forth. The factory's rich archives tell us that the painting on this vase flaked in the kiln, after it had been gilded. Rather than waste it, the enamels were removed, and Knip repainted it. She chose two birds, *Le Gros-bec Azulam* and *Le Pape*, which she could represent in low-fired pigments. Her brushwork is minutely detailed, and builds up the texture and reflective quality of the feathers with great skill.

In fact the ice-cream vases were removed from the dessert service, and were sent instead as flower vases to the King's daughter-in-law, Marie-Caroline, duchesse de Berry (1798-1870). *OF*

49. Thomas Hornor
(b. Kingston-upon-Hull 1785;
d. New York, USA 1844)

Rolling Mills
1819
Watercolour over pencil with gum
arabic on paper mounted on card,
41.4 x 54.2cm
Purchased, 1953
NMW A 3353

The accurate depiction of the Penydarren
Ironworks at Merthyr Tydfil in this image
has been dramatically enhanced by
Hornor's theatrical use of light, which
floods out of the building and the nearby
brazier. By the early nineteenth century
Wales was the greatest iron producing
country in the world. The industry was
centred on Merthyr Tydfil, where there
were no less than seven major iron
works. Hornor's view is both dramatic
and full of detail. On the right are rolling
mills driven by a beam engine, and
tramroad bogies laden with bar iron.
The bar iron would be horse-hauled via
tramroad and canal to Cardiff for export.

On 2 April 1814 Hornor advertised his
services to survey estates in Wales in
The Cambrian newspaper. Responses
came particularly from the Neath valley
and he was commissioned by landowners
to produce at least nine albums of views

in south Wales. *Rolling Mills* was
originally pasted into an album in
the Duke of Sutherland's library. The
Museum also owns an album of twenty-
five illustrations from 1816 titled
*Illustrations of the Vale of Neath with
the scenery of Rheola and part of the
adjoining Country* made for John
Edwards (1772-1833). Each album
contained a map and watercolours
alongside detailed descriptive pages of
the area. Hornor describes the process
of smelting iron in some detail in the
text accompanying this image.

Hornor worked on the south Wales
albums between 1816 and 1820. He then
began the mammoth task of making a
panorama of the whole of London from
the top of St Paul's Cathedral. By 1826
he had moved to New York, where he
worked as a topographer. *BM*

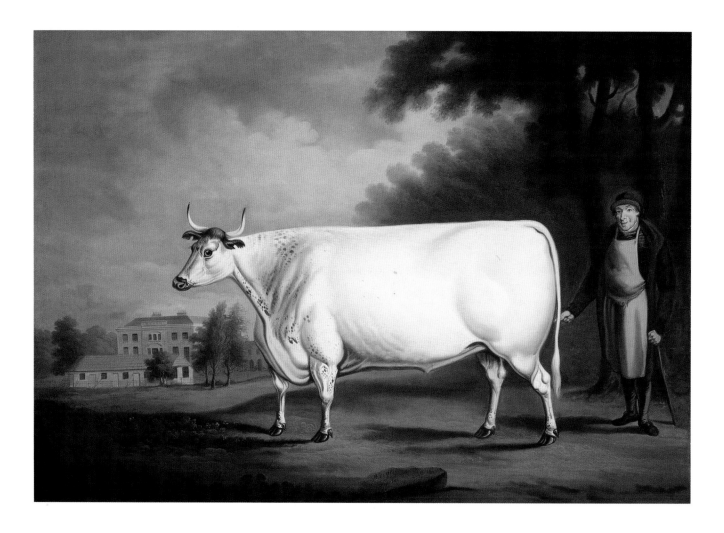

50. Daniel Clowes
(b. Chester 1774; d. Chester 1829)

The Nannau Ox
1824
Oil on canvas, 65 x 85.5cm
Purchased, 2008
NMW A 29363

The Nannau ox was slaughtered and roasted to celebrate the twenty-first birthday of Robert Williames Vaughan (1803-1859) on 25 June 1824. It was one of the last of an ancient herd of white cattle bred at Nannau, near Dolgellau in Merioneth. Beside it stands the Vaughan family cowman, Sion Dafydd.

The young man's father, Sir Robert Williames Vaughan (1768-1843), 2nd baronet, was Merioneth's biggest resident landowner and its sole representative in Parliament for over four decades. The heir's coming of age was celebrated all over north Wales with bell ringing, fireworks, cannon salutes, balloon ascents and the distribution of food and drink to the poor. The centrepiece of the day was a banquet for nearly two hundred guests. To accommodate them, a temporary wooden building covered with brown canvas and a thatched roof was put up in front of the house. This structure appears in the background of the painting, together with Nannau itself, a neo-classical house built in the 1790s. The ox supplied a huge top sirloin or 'baron' of beef, weighing 166 lbs. Its horns and hooves were later mounted in silver as a memento of the occasion.

This is one of a group of paintings of cattle, horses and dogs Sir Robert commissioned from Clowes, a Chester artist who specialised in animal and sporting subjects. It represents a number of paintings in the collection that record people and events in early nineteenth-century Wales. *OF*

51. John Constable
(b. East Burgholt, Suffolk 1776;
d. London 1837))

A Cottage in a Cornfield
1815-17
Oil on canvas, 31.5 x 26.3cm
Purchased with the assistance of
the Art Fund, 1978
NMW A 486

The subject of this small painting is
a Suffolk cottage in a cornfield, near
Constable's father's house in East
Bergholt. It is high summer, with the corn
still green in places and meadow flowers
in bloom behind the gate into the field.
In 1815 Constable was still struggling to
find an original manner of painting his
native scenery, but was just beginning
to attract the attention of critics, who
characterized his work as 'natural',
'fresh' and 'truthful', the qualities he
was seeking to achieve here.

Constable's free and spontaneous
technique established him as one of the
most celebrated landscape painters of the
nineteenth century, rivalled only by his
contemporary Turner. His later influence
was so great that his way of depicting the
English countryside now seems quite
commonplace. At the time, however,

his detailed portrayal of nature and his
skilful use of colour were completely
original. He exhibited in France during
the 1820s where his effects of light and
atmosphere were widely admired.

Despite its naturalism, the evolution of
this image was surprisingly complex.
Constable drew the scene in the summer
of 1815, and began an oil painting twice
the size of this one. He had trouble with
the tree on the right, and abandoned the
larger painting (now in the Victoria and
Albert Museum), returning to it in 1833.
When he began this smaller version,
which was exhibited at the Royal
Academy in 1817, he made many minor
changes that produced a tidier, more
formal composition. The problematic tree
was replaced by a quite different one,
apparently after an engraving. *OF*

52. Joseph Mallord William Turner
(b. London 1775; d. London 1851)

Flint Castle
1835
Watercolour with scratching out on
paper, 27.7 x 40.1cm
Accepted by H.M. Government in lieu
of inheritance tax, 1982
NMW A 1757

This watercolour was owned by the
influential writer and critic John Ruskin
(1819-1900), who championed Turner's
work. He wrote, 'This is the loveliest
piece of pure water-colour painting in my
whole collection; nor do I know anything
elsewhere that can compare, and little
that can rival, the play of light on the
sea surface and the infinite purity of
playing colour in the ripples of it as
they near the sand.'

Turner, more than any other artist,
transformed watercolour painting in
Britain. He raised the status of the
medium and expanded its technical
possibilities. His great confidence and
mastery of the medium is particularly
evident in the reflection of the setting
sun, which has probably been achieved
by using a wet sponge. He has also used
'scraping out', where he creates highlights

by scraping the pigment to reveal the
white paper below, probably using his
sharpened thumbnail.

The colours, tones and composition
combine to create an almost dreamlike,
visionary scene. The ruined castle of Flint
is seen in the background, while in the
foreground a mother and children
approach a shrimper. The image was
engraved by J. R. Kernot and published
in the *Picturesque Views in England and
Wales* series in 1836.

Turner visited Flint while on tour in
north Wales in 1794, 1798 and 1799.
He probably relied on sketches from
these visits, and his memory, for this
work. His early sketching trips to
Wales influenced his art throughout
his career. *BM*

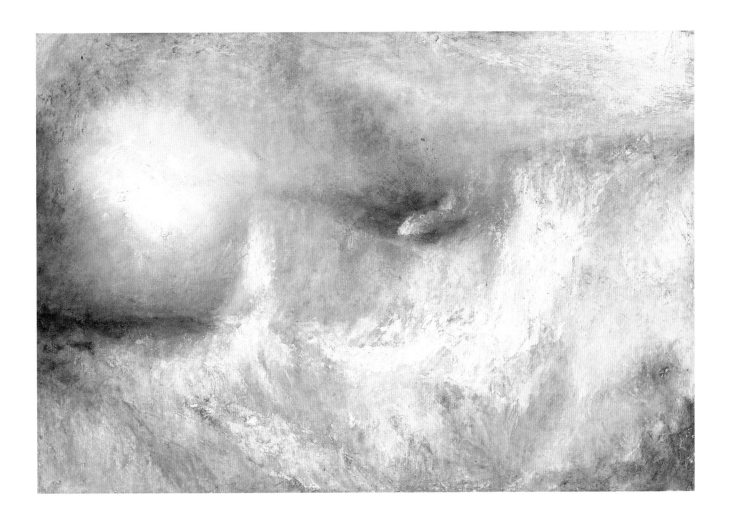

53. Joseph Mallord William Turner
(b. London 1775; d. London 1851)

The Beacon Light
About 1835-40
Oil on canvas, 61.5 x 96cm
Bequeathed by Gwendoline Davies, 1951
NMW A 433

Turner has used dramatic areas of impasto in this painting to express the spume and spray of the waves as they crash against the cliff. He is primarily interested in representing the effect of light over the raging sea and the misty atmospheric effect this creates. A warning beacon shines out and adds a splash of colour to the scene.

Turner had a long fascination with the sea and produced marine subjects throughout his career. This work is one of a small group of paintings he produced on smaller canvases, roughly half the size of his usual format. Turner made significant changes to the composition during execution, including painting out a lighthouse or tower to the right of the cliff edge. Traditionally thought to be a depiction of the Needles on the Isle of Wight, the location is now believed to be either on the Kent coast between Margate and Folkestone or near Dover.

This painting came from the collection of Sophia Caroline Booth (1798-1875), the landlady of a boarding house in Margate, with whom Turner had a long liaison. Like all the Turner oil paintings in the Museum's collection, this work was bequeathed by the Davies sisters. They had previously bought oil paintings by Turner thought to have come from the same collection and their advisor Hugh Baker (1873-1936) records securing this work for Gwendoline Davies, writing in his diary on 7 July 1922, 'Quite an exciting afternoon at Christie's. Bought Turner's Beacon Light from the Brocklebank collection for 2,500 guineas'. Then, as now, Turner's work commanded high prices, and the Davies sisters spent far more on pictures by Turner than they did on many of their Impressionist paintings. *BM*

54. Ewer and dish

Silver gilt, London, 1844-5
Designed by George Shaw and
Thomas William King

Maker's mark of John Samuel Hunt

Ewer

Height: 33.5cm; length: 14.6cm

Purchased with the assistance of the
National Heritage Memorial Fund and
the Art Fund, 1994

NMW A 51147

Dish

Diameter: 49.8 cm
Purchased, 1992

NMW A 50714

This ewer and dish were made for London lawyer Sir Samuel Rush Meyrick (1783-1848) of Goodrich Court, Herefordshire. Meyrick was obsessed with heraldry and both pieces bear the arms of supposed ancestors. The figures on the ewer may depict the legendary origin of the Meyrick arms, said to have been granted to Cadafael Ynfyd, judge at the Court of Powys in the time of Llewellyn the Great, who rallied the people by lighting beacons with a flaming staff.

The decoration on the dish is adapted from that on four thirteenth-century gemellions, or rose-water dishes, then in Meyrick's collection and now in the British Museum. They had belonged to his friend the antiquary Francis Douce (1757-1834) who regarded them as the most important mediaeval Limoges enamels in his collection. The dish was designed in 1843 by Meyrick's friends Thomas William King, a herald at the College of Arms, and the architect George Shaw.

Meyrick published his great work *A critical inquiry into antient armour as it existed in Europe* in 1824. He was consulted as to the arrangement of the national collection of arms and armour in the Tower of London, and in 1828 he arranged the collection at Windsor Castle. After trying to buy and restore the genuinely mediaeval Goodrich Castle overlooking the River Wye, he built his own fantasy castle nearby, which he called Goodrich Court, to house his collection of armour and mediaeval art. As well as filling the house with genuine antiquities, Meyrick commissioned furniture, stained glass and silver in a range of historical styles. *OF*

55. John Gibson
(b. Gyffin, Conwy, Caernarvonshire 1790; d. Rome, Italy 1866)

Aurora
1841-8

Marble, height: 172cm; width: 45.7cm

Purchased with the assistance of the Art Fund, 1993

NMW A 2527

During the 1840s John Gibson was one of the most celebrated sculptors in Europe, famous for works in marble that recalled the art of ancient Greece and Rome. He had begun his career as an apprentice to a monumental mason in Liverpool, and was helped to become a sculptor by the banker and art collector William Roscoe (1753-1831). In 1817 he settled in Rome, where he completed his training under the neo-classical sculptor Antonio Canova (1757-1822), and was also influenced by the more austere 'Greek' style of Bertel Thorvaldsen (1770-1844).

Roscoe's granddaughter Margaret and her husband Henry Sandbach visited Gibson in Rome in 1838. Margaret, who was a poet, became a close friend and critic, and Henry decided to commission a statue '...congenial with her own poetic feeling'. In July 1842 Gibson completed his life-size clay model for Aurora, goddess of the morning, and described her as 'just risen from the ocean with the bright star of Lucifer glittering over her brow – one foot on the waves, the other softly touching the earth...'.

Gibson was inspired by two lines from Milton, and had begun work on the model several months before, taking the imagery from a figure on a Greek vase. The marble was carved under his supervision by his head workman Signor Baini. Gibson charged Henry Sandbach £300 (the cost to him in marble and labour was about £110). It was originally lightly tinted, and was shown in a deep blue niche in the Sandbach's Liverpool home. It was moved to the sculpture room of their new house, Hafodunos, near Abergele, soon after. *OF*

56. David Cox
(b. Birmingham 1783;
d. Harborne, Birmingham 1859)

The Train on the Coast
About 1850

Watercolour and pencil on paper,
27 x 37.1cm

James Pyke Thompson collection
transferred from the Turner House, 1921

NMW A 1736

In this extraordinarily dynamic landscape Cox is chiefly concerned with representing the weather, light and atmosphere. As in other watercolours he produced around this time, this work confronts man and nature. The power of nature is all around, while man is represented by his technical achievement in the train on the horizon, with the steam white against the grey clouds. The remarkable freedom of handling and strong colours lends a great immediacy to the scene.

This may not be a depiction of a particular place, but rather a studio sketch, perhaps inspired by the north Wales coast line. The Chester to Holyhead railway opened in 1848 and was one which Cox would have been very familiar with, as he travelled regularly to north Wales. In 1844 he visited Betws-y-coed, writing, 'we agree to stop a week; there is no end of the fine

river scenery and rocks and mountains'. Cox was so drawn to the area that he made annual summer visits there until 1856. Other artists followed, and the village has been described as Britain's first artists' colony.

The work is painted on a coarse paper designed as a wrapping paper that Cox discovered in 1836. Cox liked working with the texture and impurities within it and a similar paper was later marketed as 'Cox' paper.

Cox trained initially in Birmingham, moving to London in 1804, where he took lessons from the watercolourist John Varley (1778-1842). He exhibited at the Royal Academy and became a member of the Society for Painters in Watercolour, submitting numerous works for their annual exhibitions. He also wrote several treatises on landscape painting and the watercolour technique. *BM*

57. William Dyce
(b. Aberdeen 1806;
d. Streatham, London 1864)

**Welsh Landscape with
Two Women Knitting**
1860
Oil on board, 34.3 x 49.5cm
Purchased with the assistance of the
National Heritage Memorial Fund, the
Art Fund, the estate of Alan Thomas,
and many private donors, 2010
NMW A 29527

The Scottish artist William Dyce was
one of the busiest and most influential
painters of his day. He visited the Conwy
valley in the autumn of 1860, where he
admired and sketched 'every variety of
Welsh scenery.' He was an important
supporter of the Pre-Raphaelites' aim
to renew English art through truth to
nature, and this picture, which was
painted on his return to London,
draws on his observations.

It is a romanticised Victorian view of
'wild Wales' and its 'unspoilt' people.
The younger woman is dressed in the
recently revived Welsh national costume,
which in reality was only worn on special
occasions. Both women are knitting
stockings from scavenged scraps of wool,
even though this was an occupation for
the home that had largely disappeared
by 1860. It is full of contrived contrasts –
between age and beauty, and between

transitory humans and ancient geological
formations – while the sickle moon
suggests the cyclical progression of the
universe.

Dyce and his family stayed for six weeks
at a hotel in Llanrwst. He was very taken
with the Conwy valley, and wrote 'I have
got some materials which I hope to turn
to good account ...these trips for a
change of air always pay'. He added,
referring to *Pegwell Bay* (Tate), his best-
known work, 'I made £400 from my trip
to Ramsgate two years ago ... and I hope
to make an equally good thing out of the
Welsh excursion.'

Dyce was only one of many Victorian
artists who worked in Snowdonia.
Following the growth of railways in the
area in the 1830s and 1840s, the Conwy
valley became a popular destination for
painters. *OF*

58. Dante Gabriel Rossetti
(b. London 1828;
d. Birchington, Kent 1882)

Fair Rosamund
1861
Oil on canvas, 51.9 x 41.7cm
James Pyke Thompson collection
transferred from the Turner House, 1921
NMW A 169

Rosamund Clifford was Henry II's mistress. According to one of the many legends surrounding her life, the King built her a hunting lodge within a maze at Woodstock, which he alone negotiated via a red silk cord. This painting is one of a series of similar works by Rossetti dating from the 1860s, all half or bust-length depictions of women, heavily influenced by sixteenth-century Venetian painting (decidedly post-Raphaelite) and with an emphasis on visual opulence and atmosphere rather than narrative.

Rosamund's identity is signified by the recurring motif of the flower *rosa mundi* (rose of the world) and the red cord. Otherwise, Rossetti shuns any storytelling aspect, emphasizing instead the sensual – flesh and fabric, colour and texture – to create a claustrophobic study of beauty and *ennui* that hangs on the twitch of a thread. The model was Rossetti's mistress Fanny Cornforth. Although the story of

Rosamund would have been well known within Rossetti's circle as part of a resurgence of interest in the medieval, it takes no great leap to connect the interminably confined Rosamund with the dreary limbo of the Victorian mistress.

Most of the works in this series were commissioned or available to a limited circle of regular buyers and, like Rosamund herself, the painting is an object of desire (Rossetti also designed the picture's frame to provide visual harmony), to be owned and admired. Both in style and subject, such an unapologetically languid depiction of a 'fallen' woman, without explanation or consequence, diverged sharply from the moralising nature of Victorian art conventions and Rossetti's own earlier Pre-Raphaelitism, heralding the Aesthetic movement's ideal of 'art for art's sake'.
BD

59. William Holman Hunt
(b. London 1827; d. London 1910)

The Golden Prime of Good Haroun Alraschid
1866, reworked in 1891
Watercolour on vellum, 10.2 x 12.7cm
James Pyke Thompson collection transferred from the Turner House, 1921
NMW A 607

*And many a sheeny summer-morn,
Adown the Tigris I was borne,
By Bagdat's shrines of fretted gold,
High-walled gardens green and old;*

These lines come from Alfred Tennyson's *Recollections of the Arabian Nights*, to which this beautiful watercolour is an illustration. The Abbasid Caliph Harun al-Raschid (763 or 766-809) ruled Baghdad and appears in romanticised form in *The 1,001 Nights*. He is shown here reclining before an imagined panorama of medieval Baghdad.

In 1857 Hunt was engaged to produce six designs for woodcut illustrations to the new edition of Tennyson's *Poems*. Hunt was then commissioned to make a drawing after this design for Thomas Emerson Crawhall (1820-1896), a Newcastle collector. Hunt had spent 1854-5 travelling in the Middle East and he responded enthusiastically to the commission, 'being anxious to intensify my conception with the glory of colour belonging to the East', as he recalled later. However he took nearly eight years to produce this watercolour and his patron seems to have lost interest.

In 1891 Hunt approached James Pyke Thompson (1846-1897), the collector and founder of the Turner House gallery in Penarth. The artist wrote: 'I should mention that I have in my hands a drawing in watercolour on vellum ... It is highly finished ... and of great delicacy, and ... fullness of colour. It is of gemlike proportions ... the price – owing to particular circumstances – is certainly exceptionally low if sold now, £75'. Hunt retouched the watercolour at this point, rendering the reflections of the boat and mosque more distinct. In his letters to Thompson he gave instruction for framing, specifying a background of 'red-blood coloured cloth'. *CT*

60. Roll-top desk

Oak, pitch pine, marquetry of various woods, semi-precious stones, glass, brass, iron

Designed by John Pollard Seddon (1827-1906) and made by Thomas Seddon (Seddon & Co), about 1862

Height: 114.1cm; length 104.7cm

Purchased, 1982

NMW A 50583

This writing desk is a sophisticated example of the Victorian Gothic style. It is extremely ornate and covered over much of its surface with medieval-inspired patterns in superbly executed marquetry that was once strikingly colourful. The architect John Pollard Seddon worked in Wales between 1853 and 1863. The initials IS, as well as roundels featuring the tools of his architectural trade, suggest that he designed the desk for his own use.

The desk is one of several pieces by Seddon shown at the 1862 International Exhibition in London. It was one of the major works in the Medieval Court, organized by Seddon's friend the architect William Burges (1827-1881). The Court was a high point of the Victorian Gothic revival, featuring designs in a medieval manner by the best progressive architects of the day.

Contemporary opinion on this desk was divided. *The Building News* criticised its excessive decoration: 'such eccentricities cannot be defended ... there is a rawness about the ornament of the whole work, which we cannot help objecting to.' *The Civil Engineer*, on the other hand, found it 'most interesting for the beauty as well as the convenience of form, and the excellent colouring produced by inlaying.'

Comparing the desk to the brightly painted furniture in the Medieval Court, Burges was not entirely complimentary. He notes that Seddon introduced colour 'by means of marquetry ... But here a curious fact is to be noticed. All Messrs. Prichard and Seddon's work which has painted figure-panels looks well ... but the little writing-table, where only marquetry is employed, by no means comes up to the mark of the others.' *RC*

61. Binding for *The Book of Common Prayer*

Silver gilt, ivory, enamel, velvet, London, 1868-9

Length 12.8cm

Purchased, 2010

NMW A 51690

Goblet

Silver, partly gilt, semi-precious stones, enamel, London, 1870-71

Height 11.8cm

Purchased, 1984

NMW A 50497

Both designed by William Burges (1827-1881) and made by Jes Barkentin

This intimate prayer book binding was created for the politician and architectural pundit Sir Alexander James Beresford Beresford Hope (1820-1887), one of Burges's leading patrons. It is mounted in ivory, which contrasts beautifully with the rich, purple velvet spine. It is studded with silver-gilt Tudor rosettes with jewel-like enamelling. The central rosette is embellished with a fantastical beast and the others are personalized with the initials 'A H' and 'I H'. The binding has two clasps, each in the form of a stylized dragon with a shield bearing the Hope coat of arms and family motto.

The goblet, made for Burges himself, is one of three known examples of a similar design. Engraved beneath the rim is the triplet 'NOSTRUM STATUM PINGIT ROSA: NOSTRI STATUS DECENS GLOSA: NOSTRAE VITAE LECTIO'.

This appears to be taken from a work by the twelfth-century poet and theologian Alanus ab Insulis. In it, Alanus describes how objects of creation are embodied with complex, emblematic meanings. The goblet incorporates colourful cameos and semi-precious stones, probably from Burges's own collection. These are mounted amid intertwining hop tendrils on the upper body, perhaps symbolizing alcohol.

The architect and designer William Burges was one of the pre-eminent figures of the Victorian Gothic revival. His fantastical vision was given free rein in Cardiff thanks to the generous patronage of the 3rd Marquess of Bute, who commissioned Burges to redesign the interiors of Cardiff Castle in 1866 and Castell Coch in 1872. Burges's silver designs are among his most eccentric, combining different styles and materials to dramatic effect. *RC*

62. Cup
Gold, London, 1867-8
Maker's mark of Robert Garrard II
Height: 39.8cm; diameter: 14.7cm
Purchased with the assistance of the
Heritage Lottery Fund, 1997
NMW A 51216

This cup is the largest known object made of Welsh gold, and a relic of the now-forgotten Merioneth gold rush of 1862. One of the few Welsh mines to produce a significant quantity of gold in the 1860s was Castell Carn Dochan, near Bala. Discovered in 1863, this lode of gold was beneath the Merioneth estate of Sir Watkin Williams-Wynn (1820-1885), 6th baronet. The mine company agreed to pay Sir Watkin a royalty of 1/12th of its production. 837 ounces of gold were produced in 1865, but in 1866 the yield began to decline, and the mine closed in 1873.

Sir Watkin was one of the wealthiest landowners in Wales and could afford to treat the Castell Carn Dochan gold as a curiosity. The cup was made of 22 carat gold (91.6% pure and the same standard as gold coins) by the firm of R. and S. Garrard & Co.

The foot is engraved 'MADE OF GOLD THE ROYALTY FROM CASTELL CORNDOCHAN. MINE. 1867.' Garrard's adapted a drawing by Hans Holbein the Younger (1497/8-1543) in the British Museum, which is a design for a cup King Henry VIII gave Queen Jane Seymour. R. N. Wornum wrote of it in 1867, 'There is no better cinque-cento ornament than this; it is the same taste as, but perhaps purer than, the best work of Benevenuto Cellini...'. The designer replaced the Renaissance medallion portraits around the bowl of the original with the Williams-Wynn eagle and fox, together with a wolf and a goat, but reproduced the remaining ornament. The cup's iconography reflects Sir Watkin's pride in his family and in the Welsh language. *OF*

63. Sir Edward Burne-Jones
(b. Birmingham 1833;
d. Fulham, London 1898)

Perseus and the Graiae
1877

Oil, bronze and silver leaf on gesso on oak panel, 152.4 x 168.7cm

Accepted by H.M. Government in lieu of Inheritance Tax, and part-purchased with the assistance of the Art Fund, 2008

NMW A 29299

In 1875 the young Conservative MP Arthur Balfour (1848-1930) commissioned a cycle of narrative works from Burne-Jones for the drawing room of 4 Carlton Gardens, London.

Burne-Jones took a poetic narrative of the Perseus legend from William Morris's *Earthly Paradise* of 1868-70. He devised a sequence of ten scenes; six were to be oil paintings and the remaining four were to be low relief panels executed largely in gesso. All ten were to be set in an elaborate framework of acanthus scrolls, also in gesso relief. Work on the oil paintings and gesso panels proceeded slowly, and Balfour had only received this relief and four oils (Staatsgalerie Stuttgart) before Burne-Jones died in 1898.

Burne-Jones concentrated on the most familiar episodes of the Perseus legend – the hero's search for the gorgon Medusa,

his killing of her and his rescue of Andromeda. To find Medusa, Perseus needed the help of the Graiae, three sisters who had only one eye between them. He stands centrally over the sisters, having stolen the eye. Above him is a long Latin inscription relating the entire story. The bodies, limbs and swirling drapery are modelled in gesso in low-relief. The heads and hands are painted in oils, while the grainy surface of the oak panel provides a barren landscape.

Burne-Jones worked on the panel with his studio assistants and the gesso-specialist Osmund Weeks. However it was not well-received when exhibited at the Grosvenor Gallery in 1878, and Burne-Jones abandoned the remaining reliefs. *OF*

64. Sir Edward Burne-Jones
(b. Birmingham 1833;
d. Fulham, London 1898)

King Arthur at Avalon (study)
About 1890
Charcoal, chalk, watercolour bodycolour
and gold paint on paper on a wooden
strainer, 96.5 x 225.2cm
Given by Sir William Goscombe John
in memory of his parents, 1926
NMW A 11747

King Arthur is shown on the magical
island of Avalon, having been mortally
wounded in battle. Legend held that he
was to lie there in a dreamlike state, until
summoned to rise again. The subject is
taken from Thomas Malory's *Morte
d'Arthur*, 1470 (book 21, chapters 5 and
6) 'Some men yet say that King Arthur is
not dead, but had by the will of our Lord
Jesus Christ into another place; and men
say that he will come again'.

Burne-Jones originally explored this
subject for a commission he received in
1881 from his friend and patron George
Howard (1843-1911) to decorate the
library at Naworth Castle, Cumberland.
The subject absorbed him and dominated
his last years. This work is a composition
study and is quite different from the final,
vast oil painting *The Sleep of Arthur in
Avalon*, 1881-98 (Museo de Arte de

Ponce, The Louis A Ferré Foundation,
Inc., Puerto Rico), which was unfinished
at the time of his death. Burne-Jones
produced hundreds of studies (see left)
in connection with this project. He said,
'it won't do to begin painting heads or
much detail in this picture till it's all
settled. I do so believe in getting in the
bones of a picture properly first, then
putting on the flesh and afterwards the
skin and then another skin; last of all
combing its hair and sending it forth
to the world'.

Burne-Jones was a pupil of Dante Gabriel
Rossetti (no. 58) and belonged to the
second generation of the Pre-Raphaelite
Brotherhood. He worked closely with
William Morris (1834-1896) and was
championed by the influential critic
John Ruskin (1819-1900). *BM*

65. James Tissot
(b. Nantes, France 1836;
d. Buillon 1902)

The Parting
1872
Oil on canvas, 68.6 x 91.4cm
Bequeathed by William Menelaus, 1882
NMW A 184

This is one of the most accomplished examples of the eighteenth-century style costume pieces Tissot painted after his arrival in London in 1871. He moved there from his native France after the failure of the Commune uprising in Paris.

Tissot anglicised his first name to James, and adapted his work to suit a British audience. Victorians enjoyed pictures with narrative, and Tissot also delighted in tension and ambiguity. Here, looking out over the Thames, two young women and a soldier show wistful dismay at his imminent departure. Behind, troops wait in a boat ready to depart, and papers on the ledge add to the plot.

The dress and interior in this image are sumptuous props rather than attempts at authenticity. Even the bow-window is

thought to have been constructed for the artist in his studio. Tissot had an affinity with British aesthetic art. His depiction of detail, textures and surfaces, for example, is comparable to that of Laurence Alma-Tadema. Friends such as Millais and Whistler were also influential.

Tissot remained close to his French contemporaries, who included the Impressionists. Of the several works relating to this painting, one is a pencil sketch of the left-hand figure, with the inscription 'à mon ami Degas' (to my friend Degas). He returned to France in 1882. This work was bought by William Menelaus for £3,900 at Christie's in 1881, and was included in his bequest to the Cardiff Museum a year later. It was therefore one of the first works of art to enter the Museum's collection. *AP*

66. Edward Lear
(b. London 1812;
d. San Remo, Italy 1888)

Kinchinjunga from Darjeeling
1877
Oil on canvas, 181.2 x 224.7cm
Purchased with the assistance of
the Art Fund, 2006
NMW A 28349

Lear arrived in Darjeeling in January 1874. As well as making sketches, he also bought photographs of the surrounding countryside, to help in the composition of this painting of Kanchenjunga, the world's third highest peak, which he began in his studio in 1875.

Lear had been commissioned by Henry Bruce (1815-1895) to paint an Indian scene of his own choice. Bruce, a Glamorgan landowner, industrialist and politician became 1st Lord Aberdare in 1873. Lear wrote to him in September 1875 'I intend that the 'Kinchinjunga' shall be so good a picture that nobody will ever be able, – if it hung in your Dining room – to eat any dinner along of contemplating it – so that the painting

will not only be a desirable but a highly economical object.' It was dispatched from Italy in May 1877, and Lear wrote to Lady Aberdare in August, 'I hope you will kindly write me a line ... to tell me how you like it. All I beg of you particularly is this, – that if it stands on the ground, you will put up a railing to prevent the children ... falling over the edge into the Abyss'.

Edward Lear is best known today as the author of nonsense verse, including *The Owl and the Pussycat* (1867), but he was an outstanding painter of landscapes, particularly of out of the way places. He had spent the years 1837-48 in Rome, where his friends included Penry Williams and John Gibson. *OF*

67. James Abbott McNeill Whistler
(b. Lowell, Massachusetts 1834;
d. London 1903)

**Nocturne: blue and gold,
St Mark's, Venice**
1880
Oil on canvas, 49.5 x 61.5cm
Bequeathed by Gwendoline Davies, 1951
NMW A 210

This atmospheric image of the basilica of St Mark's is one of only three known oil paintings of Venice by Whistler, who first visited the city following his infamous libel suit against the art critic John Ruskin in 1879. Although Whistler won his action, the symbolic award of a farthing in damages and no costs bankrupted him, and obliged him to accept a commission to make a series of etchings of Venice.

Venice had been a popular subject with painters for centuries, but Whistler was one of the first artists to depict it as a living, working city, rather than simply a grand stage set or picturesque relic. Designed to evoke mood rather than narrative detail, this view was painted from the vantage point of Café Florian, a popular meeting place on the south side of the Piazza di San Marco.

Only the essentials of the Byzantine architecture are represented as the basilica looms against the night sky, recalling the description by Henry James (a Café Florian regular) of St Mark's as 'the wonderful church, with its low domes and bristling embroideries, the mystery of its mosaic and sculpture, looking ghostly in the tempered gloom…'. Whistler's smooth, glassy brushwork is flecked with white to show the newly installed gas light in the Piazza, revealing, to the left of the façade, scaffolding erected to carry out restoration.

Whistler declared this picture as perhaps the best of his nocturnes. It was bought by Gwendoline Davies in 1912. *BD*

68. Sir Alfred Gilbert
(b. London 1854; d. London 1934)

Icarus
1884

Bronze, height: 100cm; width: 48cm

Given by Sir William Goscombe John,
1938

NMW A 116

This moody, pensive youth is Icarus, the mythical son of the Greek inventor Daedelus. Provided with wings of wax and feathers by his father, Icarus flew too near the sun and crashed to the earth when the wax melted. The bird on the base, which is about to be devoured by a snake, echoes his fate. The bronze was commissioned for £100 from Gilbert, then the most exciting new talent in sculpture, by Frederic Leighton (1831-1896), President of the Royal Academy. Leighton, a painter who had himself made a small number of vigorously lifelike bronzes, left the choice of subject to Gilbert.

Gilbert had lived in Rome since 1878, and had found his inspiration not in classical art but in the work of Renaissance sculptors, especially Donatello, Verrochio and Cellini. He later claimed that Icarus, often a personification of the dangers of youthful ambition, was his favourite work and that it represented his ability to soar over all earthly obstacles at the beginning of his career.

This statue, inspired by Donatello's *David*, created a sensation at the Royal Academy in 1884, and is one of the finest British bronzes of the nineteenth century. It was cast by Gilbert himself using the *cire perdue* (lost wax) method. It had a particular importance to the artists who learnt from it over the next twenty years, and whose work is now called the 'New Sculpture.' One of these was Sir William Goscombe John, who bought *Icarus* in 1935 and gave it to the National Museum. *OF*

© Michael Cox

69. Sir William Goscombe John
(b. Cardiff 1860; d. London 1952)

St John the Baptist
About 1894
Bronze, height: 208cm; width: 85cm
Purchased by the Cardiff Museum, 1904
NMW A 2519

In 1874 William Goscombe John joined the workshops established by John Crichton-Stuart, 3rd Marquess of Bute (1847-1900), to make decorative work for William Burges's remodelling of Cardiff Castle. Meanwhile he attended drawing and modelling classes at Cardiff School of Art before becoming a pupil assistant to Thomas Nicholls, a London sculptor also working for Burges.

This sculpture is from a model commissioned by Lord Bute in 1892. Bute was a passionate convert to Catholicism, and the subject is his patron saint. The first cast, for the garden of his London house in Regent's Park, was in burnished pewter rather than bronze. It represents the saint, the forerunner of Christ, unkempt and dressed in a tunic of animal skins knotted at the waist.

He stands on a rock, preaching to the multitude (Luke 3: 1-17), 'a voice crying aloud in the wilderness'.

The full-size plaster was exhibited at the Royal Academy in 1894. Goscombe John was a member of the 'New Sculpture' movement and greatly influenced by Alfred Gilbert. He built a formidable international reputation by 1900, but his career was based on his careful manipulation of local support. Bute was one of those who helped fund his travels in 1889-90, when he spent a year in Paris studying the working methods of his French contemporaries. This over-life-size figure was his most ambitious work to date, and he would have known that Rodin had tackled the same subject, *St John Preaching* (no. 85), on the same scale in 1878-80. *OF*

70. Lionel Walden
(b. Norwich, Connecticut, USA 1861;
d. Chantilly, France 1933)

Steelworks, Cardiff at Night
1893-7
Oil on canvas, 150.8 x 200.4cm
Given by the artist, 1920
NMW A 2245

A train gets up steam in the steelworks that light up the night in this massive industrial scene. The Dowlais-Cardiff Works was built on Cardiff East Moors in 1887-97. It was the earliest of the new Welsh steel industry's works to be sited near the docks, replacing older works in Valleys locations. The brainchild of Edward Martin (1844-1910), who had succeeded William Menelaus as the General Manager of the Dowlais Iron Company, its scale and novel layout attracted international attention. Iron ore landed at Cardiff Docks could be made into steel bars within forty-eight hours.

Walden was obviously fascinated by the industrial life and scenery of Cardiff, which he painted several times. One of the resulting paintings, *Cardiff Docks*, was exhibited at the Salon in Paris in 1896, where it was purchased by the French state (Musée d'Orsay). It is believed to be a pair with this painting and is of similar size and subject. This work is based on an oil sketch, perhaps captured on the spot and also in the Museum's collection *(Sketch for Steel Works, Cardiff at Night*, NMW A 2054). Walden also presented a large painting of Cardiff docks.

Walden moved to Paris from America as a young man and studied there under Emile Auguste Carolus-Duran (1838-1917). In Paris he was a frequent contributor to the Salon and won a medal in 1903. He exhibited at the Cardiff Fine Art Society in 1893 and at the Royal Academy in 1897. In 1911 he visited Hawaii; he went on to spend much of his time there and became known for his seascapes, capturing the many moods of the sea in differing light conditions. *BM*

71. John Singer Sargent
(b. Florence, Italy 1856;
d. London 1925)

Figure Study
About 1900

Watercolour, pencil and
chalk on paper, 48.4 x 54.7cm

Given by Sir William Goscombe John,
1940

NMW A 2610

Shown in an informal setting, probably the artist's London studio, the model lies back, perhaps sleeping, with one arm looped through some drapery. The relaxed nature of the pose is deceptive; it is carefully composed, in close imitation of the famous sculpture the *Barberini Faun*, c. 220 BC (Glyptothek, Munich). The highlights on the model's chest, raised arm and legs created by leaving the paper exposed suggest the blanched marble of the antique original.

Sargent gave the picture to the Welsh sculptor Sir William Goscombe John (1860-1952), who no doubt would have appreciated its sculptural inspiration. The inscription in the upper right reads 'to my friend Goscombe John / John S Sargent'.

From his student days in Paris, Sargent consistently made drawings from the nude model. In 1890 he was commissioned to design a series of murals for the Boston Public Library, Massachusetts.

This inspired hundreds of figure studies in preparation for the commission, though many are unrelated to the final designs. The muscular male form held particular fascination for Sargent. Here the body is sketched in pencil, while strokes of greenish wash suggest the play of muscles beneath the skin. The swirling wet washes of rich colour are typical of the artist's sumptuous watercolour technique. Sargent used watercolour increasingly from about 1900, finding endless possibilities in the medium's naturally fluid, expressive properties.

Born in Italy to an expatriate American family, Sargent was an inveterate traveller all his life. He achieved international renown as high society's portrait painter of choice by the 1890s. After 1900 he concentrated increasingly on major mural commissions, landscape painting and watercolour. *CT*

72. Jean-Baptiste-Camille Corot
(b. Paris, France 1796; d. Paris 1875)

**Castel Gandolfo, dancing Tyrolean
Shepherds by Lake Albano**
1855-60
Oil on canvas, 49.2 x 65.5cm
Bequeathed by Gwendoline Davies, 1951
NMW A 2443

Castel Gandolfo is the papal summer
residence that overlooks Lake Albano,
south of Rome. Artists have painted there
since the seventeenth century, including
the classical master Claude. Corot's first
depictions of the palace date from the
1820s during the first of three visits to
Italy. He followed the traditional path
of academic landscape painters, studying
the historic sites and scenery of Rome
and the Campagna. It was then he
began experimenting painting outdoors,
en plein air.

This work is typical of Corot's mature
style. The delicate brushwork and
shimmering variations in the silvery light
demonstrate his experience of painting
directly from nature. He began this
canvas over ten years after his last visit
to Italy, however, and the composition
was formed mainly from memory and
imagination.

Corot's interpretation of light and nature
revolutionised French landscape painting,
inspiring artists like the Impressionists.

But he also adapted his style to
academic tastes. This example is
especially reminiscent of classical
Claudean scenes with its layers of
landscape and light, the vista framed
by foliage, and the picturesque dancers
adding colour and movement.

By the end of his life Corot was widely
respected by artists of all schools. Some
works were exhibited in the Louvre
where Margaret Davies admired 'The
beautiful light in them all, and the
softness, and the touch of colour which
the figures give.' Gwendoline Davies
purchased this painting in London in
October 1909. Misleadingly it was given
the title *Castel Gandolfo, with Tyrolean
Shepherds Dancing by Lake Albano*.
Geographically it seems more likely
the shepherds were intended to be
'Tivolian'. At £6,350 this was one of
the most expensive works in the sisters'
collection. *AP*

73. Jean-Louis-Ernest Meissonier
(b. Lyon, France 1815; d. Paris 1891)

Innocents and Card Sharpers
1861
Oil on board, 24.2 x 32.2cm
Bequeathed by Margaret Davies, 1963
NMW A 2471

This painting is also known as *Innocents and Sly Ones*. It shows the fresh-faced 'innocents' on the right coming up against the more experienced, bearded 'card sharpers' on the left in a game of piquet, an early sixteenth-century trick-taking card game. Meissonier painted in microscopic detail, depicting either eighteenth-century bourgeois, or, as in the present work, cavalrymen of the Louis XIII period. His work was popular in France during the Second Empire of Napoleon III, and through his small, historic genre scenes he gained public and state acclaim and was the first artist to receive the Grand Cross of the Legion of Honour in 1889.

Historically, card-playing has been a popular subject in Western art, providing as it does a context for drama, emotion and narrative (see no.13). Meissonier evokes a considerable tension as the two young men choose their next move –

there is even perhaps the threat of violence, as the figure to the right places a hand on his sword, as if anticipating a scuffle. The compositional device of a central table balanced either side by figures was a favourite of Meissonier's, though he usually involved just two figures rather than a more complex group such as this.

Meissonier was hyper-conservative, and his particular brand of photographic realism and historical subject matter was in many ways the antithesis of progressive forms of art in France at the time, in particular the work of his contemporaries Gustave Courbet and Edouard Manet. However, his commercial popularity in the early twentieth century was considerable. Margaret Davies had admired 'the fineness of his painting' when in Paris in 1909, and she paid the formidable price of £5,250 for this work in 1910. *BD*

74. Honoré Daumier
(b. Béziers, France 1808;
d. Valmondois 1879)

Don Quixote Reading
1865-7

Oil on canvas, 82.2 x 65.0cm

Bequeathed by Gwendoline Davies, 1951

NMW A 2454

Don Quixote, the seventeenth-century novel by Cervantes, was one of Daumier's favourites. Here he illustrates an early stage in the story. Don Quixote sits engrossed in one of the chivalric romances that inspired him to embark on his own fantastical adventures. In the doorway behind, the village priest and the barber Master Nicholas observe his growing obsession and plot to destroy his books.

As in many of Daumier's paintings, the figures loom from a dark brown background with the essential features delineated by a shaft of light. Only Don Quixote's legs and the books by his side have been fully rendered, while the rest of the image has been abandoned unfinished.

Daumier began his career as a caricaturist and graphic artist. In his paintings, too, it was his mastery of line that defined his

skill. His influence was widespread. The motif of the sitting man, for example, appears in Paul Cézanne's early portrait of his father (National Gallery, London). Daumier's paintings of Don Quixote on horseback also inspired Pablo Picasso. This painting of the character reading was particularly important to Edgar Degas, its first owner. He possessed over three hundred of Daumier's lithographs, but this was his only painting by the artist.

The sale of Degas's collection after his death in 1917 did not acknowledge the painting's subject as Don Quixote. When it was purchased from Bernheim Jeune in 1918 by Gwendoline Davies it had the title *Homme assis dans un fauteuil* (Man Sitting in an Armchair). Other titles included *The Prisoner*. Its original subject was identified after it was bequeathed to the Museum in 1951. *AP*

75. Jean François Millet
(b. Greville, France 1814;
d. Barbizon 1875)

The Peasant Family
1871-2
Oil on canvas, 110.4 x 81cm
Bequeathed by Margaret Davies, 1963
NMW A 2473

Millet's early 'realist' images of rural life had caused controversy but by the end of his life his work was widely revered. *The Peasant Family* was purchased in 1911 by Margaret Davies, who had admired his paintings in the Louvre Museum in Paris.

Millet experimented with a number of drawings over several years before beginning the final canvas. The sketches skilfully delineate the anatomy of the figures and reveal his academic training and the breadth of his technique. In the final painting, however, Millet deliberately used rough brushwork and earthy colours to reflect the rustic nature of his subject. Although unfinished it remains an imposing image.

To many at that time rural life appeared simple, traditional and unchanging amid the political and social upheaval pervading most of France in the nineteenth century. Millet's peasant figures had come to symbolise moral strength and the roots of French society. This stalwart family conveys both unity and pride as they stand together in front of their humble home, holding one another firmly. At their sides, the woman's spinning tools and the man's spade are a reminder of their devotion to their work and an inherent connection to the French soil.

The picture also expresses religious ideals, for example the traditional notion of Adam digging and Eve spinning. There are also similarities to images of the Holy Family, and the child's outstretched arms might refer to the Crucifixion. Other aspects relate to ancient society. Millet is said to have owned an ancient Egyptian carved head, which could have been the inspiration for the man. All these varied allusions reinforce the notion of the monumental and iconic image Millet wished to create. *AP*

76. Edouard Manet
(b. Paris, France 1832; d. Paris 1883)

Effect of Snow at Petit-Montrouge
1870
Oil on canvas, 61.6 x 50.4cm
Bequeathed by Gwendoline Davies, 1951
NMW A 2468

With his progressive approach to both technique and subject matter, Edouard Manet is generally regarded as one of the most significant figures in nineteenth-century European painting.

In September 1870 the Prussian Army laid siege to Paris in a move that ended the Franco-Prussian war, and Manet was conscripted into the French National Guard. In late December of that year he visited his brother Eugène, also a guardsman, at Petit Montrouge on the outskirts of the city. This work shows the church of St Pierre de Montrouge, which was being used as a field hospital.

The siege lasted four months. Manet wrote that he planned to 'start some sketches from life'. Although the drab, almost monochrome palette would have been a result of his restricted circumstances, the sepia tones articulate a bleakness that reflects Manet's experience more generally. He wrote of the bitter cold and hunger, and also of the crushing boredom – a rarely depicted aspect of conflict. It has been suggested that it was Manet's first 'Impressionist' work, meaning that it was done on the spot directly onto the canvas – there is no under-drawing present, and the hastily applied brushstrokes suggest form rather than describe it. Manet inscribed the painting 'A mon ami H. Charlet' while the paint was still wet, possibly a dedication to a fellow guardsman. This work was purchased by Gwendoline Davies in 1912, the first year in which she and Margaret began buying Impressionist art. At a time when their only Impressionist purchases were the more visually arresting scenes of Venice by Monet, this work was a bold and unusual choice: but, as it transpired, a far-sighted one. *BD*

77. Pierre Auguste Renoir
(b. Limoges, France 1841;
d. Cagnes-sur-Mer 1919)

La Parisienne
1874
Oil on canvas, 163.5 x 108.5cm
Bequeathed by Gwendoline Davies, 1951
NMW A 2495

La Parisienne is the actress Henriette Henriot (1857-1944), who often posed for Renoir. Although known popularly now and in its day as *La Dame en Bleu*, or *The Blue Lady*, the title *La Parisienne* is vital to understanding the painting, its milieu and the Impressionist interest in 'modern' subjects. Renoir presents the viewer with a 'type': a fashionable, urban woman – a 'modern' woman. Her outdoor day costume is an up-to-the-minute ensemble in a shade of blue commercially available owing to recent development in synthetic dyes. She looks directly at us with confidence, meeting and holding our gaze. This overt conveyance of modernity, which would have been immediately recognisable to a contemporary audience, is a visual manifestation of the societal shift that France was undergoing at the time.

The painting has a neutral-toned background against which the sitter is suspended as if in a fashion plate that recalls the portraits and single figure compositions of Manet (whose works in turn recall Velazquez) and also the influence of Japanese prints. However, both under- and over-painting show that Renoir's original concept for the painting was somewhat different. X-ray photography reveals the original presence of a vertical form, possibly a doorway to the left of the work, and what appears to be drapery, or a curtain, to the right, suggesting a conventional portrait background was originally intended.

La Parisienne was exhibited at the so-called First Impressionist exhibition of 1874. It received mixed reviews, yet by the time Gwendoline Davies purchased it in 1913 for £5,000, it was generally considered to be one of Renoir's masterpieces. *BD*

78. Berthe Morisot
(b. Bourges, France 1841;
d. Passy 1895)

At Bougival
1882
Oil on canvas, 60 x 73.1cm
Bequeathed by Margaret Davies, 1963
NMW A 2491

This painting shows the artist's daughter, Julie, with her nanny in a garden at Bougival, ten miles west of Paris, where Morisot and her family rented a house from 1881. Because of its proximity to the city, Bougival was a popular location with the Impressionist circle, and artists including Monet, Renoir and Sisley also painted there.

Morisot was one of the exhibitors at the first Impressionist exhibition of 1874. She came from a family who encouraged her art and, although the pressures of bourgeois convention led her to marry (Edouard Manet's brother, Eugène), this enabled her to pursue her career as an artist. Yet while Morisot was working at the forefront of progressive technique, her experience of what constituted 'modern life' would have been rather different to that of her male counterparts. According to the social conventions and restraints on an upper middle-class woman, key aspects of Impressionism –

the life of the city and the flâneur, for example – were closed to her. Thus her work centres largely on explicitly 'female' subjects like portraiture, landscape and mother and child depictions.

The gardens at Bougival were a regular feature in her work, and this was painted in the garden of Dr Robin, a neighbour. The handling is exceptionally free and the variegated directional brushwork articulates perfectly the sense of a wild, shaded garden in summer as the two figures are framed and almost consumed by their surroundings. The blue, brown and white tones of the figures are dispersed throughout the canvas (which receives only a scant covering in the outer parts), giving unity to the formal structure.

Morisot exhibited in every Impressionist exhibition but one; *At Bougival* featured in the seventh, in 1882. *BD*

79. Paul Cézanne
(b. Aix-en Provence, France 1839;
d. Aix-en Provence 1906)

The François Zola Dam
About 1877-8
Oil on canvas, 54.2 x 74.2cm
Bequeathed by Gwendoline Davies, 1951
NMW A 2439

The François Zola Dam, seen here through the heat of the Provençal landscape, lies about 5km north-west of Aix-en-Provence. By this point in his career Cézanne was spending most of time in his native Provence, where he divided his time between Aix and L'Estaque.

The painting is ingeniously tight in its construction. The central 'S' arrangement, instigated by the row of cypresses in the foreground, tapers to the mountain beyond, while a vertical anchor is provided to the left by the tree, the box-like form and the geometric grey area (the dam itself) directly above it. The red-roofed house is probably an invention, designed to provide rhyming contours with the blue mountain behind. In the words of Roger Fry (1866-1934), who championed Cézanne in Britain, it reconciles 'the opposing claims of design and the total vision of nature'. He described it as '…one of the greatest of all Cézanne's landscapes, and I dare hardly say how high a place that gives it for me in all known examples of landscape art.'

In 1921, this painting, which had been owned by Gauguin, sparked a controversy regarding the reception of modernism in Britain. As Cézanne's reputation was by now well established on the continent, Gwendoline Davies, who had acquired it in Paris in 1918, offered it on loan to the National Gallery and the Tate Gallery. It was rejected by both institutions. The ensuing outcry in which *The Burlington Magazine* asserted that 'a Gallery of Modern Foreign art without a Cézanne is like a gallery of Florentine art without Giotto' forced the Tate to capitulate, and it duly went on display in 1922, for sixteen years. *BD*

80. Paul Cézanne

(b. Aix-en Provence, France 1839;
d. Aix-en Provence 1906)

The Diver
1866-9
Watercolour, bodycolour and pencil on
paper, 15.6 x 16.2cm
Bequeathed by Gwendoline Davies, 1951
NMW A 1683

'I must buy myself a box of watercolours
to work with when I'm not at my oil
painting' Cézanne wrote to his friend,
the critic and novelist Emile Zola (1840-
1902) in 1866.

This scene of a lone figure diving into
water has a mysterious, brooding
atmosphere. Is it a luminous moon or an
orange sun lighting the scene? The sex
of the diver is ambiguous; the muscular
body suggests it is more likely to be a
man, yet there is also the curvature of
a breast. In the past the work has also
been titled the *Fall of Icarus* and *Woman
diving into the Water*. The back of the
sheet has an unrelated pencil study. It
has recently been suggested that these
are portraits of the artist's father, in a
long coat and cap, gazing downwards.

Related to it is a pencil sketch of a
plunging male figure drawn from two
different angles, *Study of Nudes Diving*,
1866-8 (Los Angeles County Museum
of Art, Mr and Mrs William Preston
Harrison Collection).

Despite an early interest in art, Cézanne's
family wanted him to become a lawyer,
but he rejected this career. Much of
Cézanne's work concerned figures in
landscapes, particularly on the theme of
the Bathers. Although he did not receive
great recognition in his lifetime, he is
now recognised as a key figure in the
development of Modernism. Picasso
said of him 'My one and only master...
Cézanne was like the father of us all'.
BM

81. Vincent van Gogh
(b. Groot Zundert, Netherlands 1853;
d. Auvers-sur-Oise, France 1890)

Rain – Auvers
1890
Oil on canvas, 50.3 x 100.2cm
Bequeathed by Gwendoline Davies, 1951
NMW A 2463

This image of wheat fields is one of thirteen paintings of the countryside around Auvers van Gogh painted between 17 and 27 July 1890. In May of that year he had moved from an asylum in Provence to the town of Auvers-sur-Oise, north of Paris. He described the 'immense plain with wheat fields against the hills' and recorded painting 'immense expanses of wheat beneath troubled skies and I have not hesitated to express sadness, extreme solitude.' Fearing that he was a burden to his brother Theo, he shot himself on 27 July, just days after completing this painting.

The painting demonstrates van Gogh's interest in Japanese print techniques, which he had first encountered in Antwerp in 1885. Following his move to Paris in 1886 he began to collect *ukiyo-e* prints, and in 1887 he made a copy of Hiroshige's *Ohashi Bridge in the Rain*,

gaining insight into how to describe the sensation of rain through the medium of paint. In this work van Gogh illustrates the driving, wind-blown rain through bold downward strokes cutting through the surface impasto. The influence of Japanese prints can also be seen in the division of the picture plane into blocks of colour, demarcating the fields, village and sky.

Rain – Auvers was exhibited in *Manet and the Post Impressionists* at the Grafton Galleries in December 1910, the landmark exhibition organized by the critic Roger Fry. Known historically as the First Post-Impressionist exhibition, it is often cited as the catalyst for modernism in Britain. *Rain – Auvers* was bought by Gwendoline Davies in April 1920, and was, significantly, one of the first van Gogh works to enter a British collection. *BD*

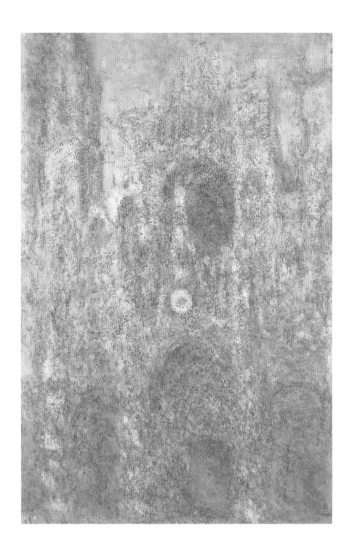

82. Claude Monet
(b. Paris, France 1840;
d. Giverny 1926)

**Rouen Cathedral: Setting Sun
(Symphony in Grey and Pink)**
1892-4
Oil on canvas, 100 x 65cm
Bequeathed by Gwendoline Davies, 1951
NMW A 2482

In February 1892 Monet began painting views of the magnificent western façade of Rouen Cathedral. His aim was to capture the effects of changing light and atmosphere on this elaborate masterwork of gothic architecture. It became one of the artist's most challenging projects.

Monet rented a studio opposite, above a novelty shop at 23 Place de la Cathédrale, where he worked relentlessly for over two months. Painting in 'series', he worked on as many as nine canvases at once – each for a different time of day – but was hampered by the changing weather. In April he returned home exasperated, writing to his dealer Paul Durand-Ruel, 'I set my sights too high and I've managed to spoil what was good.' He nonetheless returned the following February to continue. The finishing touches were completed in 1894 in his home studio in Giverny.

This sunset view of the cathedral was among those begun in 1892. The thick impasto paint surface is due in part to Monet's constant attempts to rework and perfect. But he was also conscious of his paintings' independent technical structure. Each one is an intense exercise in brushwork and colour variation. Here, the architectural detail of the image dissolves in the diminishing light of sunset, becoming atmospheric and almost abstract.

Monet eventually exhibited twenty Rouen Cathedral paintings, including this one, at Durand-Ruel's Paris gallery in May 1895, to much critical acclaim. The writer Georges Clemenceau (1841-1929) even invited the French President to buy them for the nation, but in vain. Not all the works from the exhibition were sold initially, partly due to Monet's high prices. This one remained in Monet's possession until 1913. Gwendoline Davies purchased it in 1917 for £1,350.
AP

83. Alfred Sisley
(b. Paris, France 1839;
d. Moret-sur-Loing 1899)

Storr's Rock, Lady's Cove, evening
1897
Oil on canvas, 65.5 x 81.5cm
Purchased with the assistance of the Art
Fund, 2004
NMW A 26362

Storr's Rock is a mighty limestone
outcrop, situated in a small inlet at
Langland Bay, Gower. The sunlight from
the west across the pitted surface of the
rock shows that this is the evening low
tide. The diminutive figure of a child
indicates the rock's sheer bulk. Influenced
by Claude Monet's ideas of painting in
series, Sisley painted the rock at different
times of the day, exploring the changes
in atmospheric conditions and the
fluctuating moods of the sea.

Born in Paris to parents of English
origins, Sisley was the only Impressionist
painter to work in Wales. He visited in
July 1897, staying initially at Penarth,
near Cardiff, where he painted shipping
in the Bristol Channel and the cliffs
beyond the town. His purpose was not
merely professional; he travelled with
his companion of thirty years, Eugénie
Lescouezec (1834-1898), and on
5 August they married in Cardiff,

enabling their two adult children to
be recognized as legitimate heirs.

On 13 August the Sisleys moved to
Langland Bay, lodging at the prestigious
Osborne Hotel overlooking Storr's Rock.
Despite the hotel's reputation, Sisley was
unimpressed. He wrote to a friend that
'the beds have to be seen and felt to be
believed' and that the food was either
'bad' or 'less bad'. The landscape proved
more inspiring; he wrote that the sea was
'superb and all the subjects interesting'.

On 4 October 1897 the French
newspaper *Le Journal* reported that 'the
Impressionist master has brought back
from Penarth and Langland Bay a series
of remarkable sea pieces … rendered
with an art that is as captivating as it
is personal'. Sisley's Welsh landscapes
remained little known for many years,
but are now recognised as masterpieces
of his later career. *CT*

84. Edgar Degas
(b. Paris, France 1834;
d. Paris 1917)

Dressed Dancer, study
About 1879; cast about 1922
Bronze, 71.7 x 28.25 x 27cm
Bequeathed by Gwendoline Davies, 1951
NMW A 2457

This bronze was cast from a study for Degas's famous sculpture *Little Dancer, Aged Fourteen*. The finished version was exhibited to much furore at the Sixth Impressionist Exhibition in Paris in 1881. The artist frequently made sculpture in his studio but this was the only time he formally exhibited it.

The completed original (National Gallery of Art, Washington DC) is made of wax with real hair tied in a ribbon, a linen bodice, satin shoes and a muslin tutu, displayed in a glass case. In the 1880s, a time when most sculpture was derived from the idealised form of classical nudes, this hyper-realism would have been astonishing.

Just as he and the other Impressionists had already portrayed the reality of modern life in paint, now Degas applied similar principles to sculpture. In this study in particular he accentuated his model's imperfections. Her childish form stands a little off balance, her features

seem distorted and her expression remote. His view of her is impersonal and objective; a scientific observation.

The model was a Belgian named Marie van Goethen. She was one of the dance students at the Paris Opera, commonly known as 'Opera Rats'. Ballet dancers were then perceived as low-life. Darwinian theories of evolution and popular ideas linking physiognomy to morality and intellect even led some to consider such people sub-human. At the exhibition, visitors were appalled at the 'bestial' appearance of Degas's dancer.

After Degas's death over 150 pieces of sculpture were discovered in his studio, many broken and disintegrating. The founder Adrien-Aurélien Hébrard was given permission to make a limited number of bronze casts from seventy-four of them. Gwendoline Davies purchased this rare first edition in London in 1923.
AP

85. Auguste Rodin
(b. Paris, France 1840;
d. Meudon, near Paris 1917)

St John Preaching
About 1880; cast about 1902
Bronze, 206 x 54 x 124cm
Given by Margaret Davies, 1940
NMW A 2497

The original plaster version of this sculpture was exhibited at the Paris Salon exhibition of 1880. The subject of John the Baptist was not uncommon among academic sculptures; however, their youthful idealised figures were quite different from the sinews of Rodin's aging man. The sculpture shows Rodin's style at its most realistic, at a time when his reputation was beginning to flourish. In 1877 he had been accused of making casts from a living person. As a result, St John was made larger than life-size, but no less naturalistic.

Studies for the work were prepared in separate sections, possibly using different sitters, and the head was exhibited independently in 1879. The main identified model was an Italian, César Pignatelli, who had no experience of posing. On seeing him take up a walking stance the artist wrote 'I thought immediately of a St John the Baptist; that is, a man of nature, a visionary, a believer, a forerunner come to announce one greater than himself.'

Spreading the man's weight evenly over both legs deliberately contradicted artistic convention. It was a turning point in the artist's technique as he began to sculpt from his models' spontaneous movements rather than static poses.

Rodin rarely included clothes or props in case they detracted from the essence of his figures; however, the original plaster of St John held a cross. Fortunately it was done away with in the bronze. The strong gesture and open mouth already convey intense meaning and character.

Although a devout Christian, Margaret Davies was clearly undeterred by Rodin's provocative realism when she purchased this bronze in Paris in 1917. It was cast by Alexis Rudier, Rodin's founder since 1902. *AP*

86. Auguste Rodin
(b. Paris, France 1840;
d. Meudon, near Paris 1917)

The Kiss
About 1887, cast after 1905
Bronze, 182.9 x 112 x 112cm
Given by Gwendoline Davies, 1940
NMW A 2499

The Kiss is one of Rodin's most famous works, and a widely recognized emblem of love. Its emotional intensity and technical mastery helped establish his reputation as the greatest French sculptor of the nineteenth century.

The lovers depicted are Paolo Malatesta and Francesca da Rimini, from Dante's poem *The Inferno*. Their love was kindled as they sat reading the legends of Lancelot and Guinevere. But Francesca was married to Paolo's brother Gianciotto, and at the moment they kissed her husband discovered and murdered them both. In the sculpture only the book in Paolo's hand suggests a narrative. The figures appear timeless, expressing the universal significance of their embrace.

The concept came from a project Rodin titled *The Gates of Hell*, a commission to design a large entrance to a new museum with *The Inferno* as its theme. The building never came to fruition, but Rodin carried on developing individual motifs. Other examples, such as *Eve* and *The Earth and the Moon* (see left), are also in the Museum's collection.

The Kiss was first exhibited in Paris in 1887 as a plaster model half this size, and the French State commissioned the first of three larger marble versions. Rodin's founder Alexis Rudier made a mould from the marble in 1905, from which this bronze was later cast. Both Rudier's and Rodin's marks are visible on the base. Gwendoline Davies bought it in 1912, and loaned it for public display in Cardiff and Bath before giving it to the Museum in 1940.

The purchase was both shrewd and bold. Rodin's reputation was not well established in Britain and *The Kiss* shocked some audiences – in 1913 a marble displayed in Lewes had to be covered with a sheet. However, in Cardiff the bronze was described as 'one of the greatest and most awe-inspiring works of art of modern times.' *AP*

Art from the first half of the twentieth century

The Davies collection of French art extends into the first decade of the twentieth century with late works by Monet and Cézanne, but ends with Vlaminck, Derain and Bonnard. Although there are no major Cubist works in the collection, a small Picasso still-life of 1948 was purchased in 2009, joining the German Expressionist paintings bought during the 1970s. Surrealism is an area of greater strength, with paintings by Magritte and Max Ernst as well as by British Surrealists of the 1930s, including Merlyn Evans and Ceri Richards.

By 1900, many British artists had absorbed the lessons of Impressionism, and the collection is rich in the work of those associated with the New English Art Club. Pictures by Sickert and the Camden Town Group are among the modern British works bought by Margaret Davies in the 1950s and included in her bequest in 1963. Augustus and Gwen John are central to the early twentieth-century collection. The Davies sisters had discovered Augustus back in 1916, just as his early reputation as a modernist was beginning to falter. The residue of his studio collection was bought in 1972, and he is now represented by nearly 1,400 works. His sister Gwen was almost unknown in Wales in her lifetime. Since 1935 the Museum has assembled twelve oil paintings, and also bought over a thousand drawings from her estate in 1976, which are some of the best-loved and most used that we have.

The Museum acquired work from Bernard Leach as early as 1924, and has since built a good representation of twentieth-century studio pottery. An important group designed by Susie Cooper is at the centre of the collection of twentieth-century industrial ceramics. Stone carvings by Jacob Epstein, Eric Gill and others illustrate the influences of the 'primitive' and the practice of direct carving on British sculpture after 1900, and these are accompanied by the work of European contemporaries, among them Lipschitz and Archipenko.

The collection contains many works by Cedric Morris and David Jones, members of the modernist Seven and Five Society in the later 1920s, and abstraction and international modernism in the 1930s are represented by Ben Nicholson, John Piper and others. Not surprisingly, given the importance of Wales in the British landscape tradition, the collection is also strong in neo-Romantic art of the late 1930s and the 1940s.

Right: detail from *Still-life with Poron* by Pablo Picasso (No. 94)

87. Paul Cézanne
(b. Aix-en Provence, France 1839;
d. Aix-en Provence 1906)

Still life with Teapot
1902-06

Oil on canvas, 61.4 x 74.3cm

Bequeathed by Gwendoline Davies, 1951

NMW A 2440

This still life was painted in Cézanne's last studio in Aix-en-Provence. In these final years of his life he produced some of his most important and influential paintings. Here he uses the traditional subject of the still life to explore fundamental questions about art and representation. The props have been arranged carefully against a heavy cloth, the folds giving a sense of objects nestling in a landscape.

Cézanne often painted works over a number of years, and revisions and changes were integral to his creative process. This level of attention was mirrored in the way he arranged the studio props. The young painter Louis Le Bail described his preparations for a still life: 'Cézanne arranged the fruits, contrasting the tones one against the other, making the complementaries vibrate, the greens against the reds, the yellows against the blue, tipping, turning, balancing the fruits as he wanted them to be, using coins of one or two sous for the purpose.'

In this picture the table leans slightly to the left and up towards the viewer. The knob of the teapot lid has been left out, perhaps to mirror the circular forms of the adjacent apples. Accuracy seems to be less important than the expression of balance and harmony between the various elements in the painting. Form and colour are no longer used to merely represent the visible world, but instead have an expressive power in their own right. This sense of autonomy for art, which was to become so important to the subsequent development of modernism, is hinted at in Cézanne's famous statement of 1897: 'Art is a harmony parallel to nature.' *NT*

88. Claude Monet

(b. Paris, France 1840;
d. Giverny 1926)

Waterlilies
1908
Oil on canvas, 100.7 x 81.3cm
Bequeathed by Gwendoline Davies, 1951
NMW A 2480

This was one of forty-eight paintings of waterlilies shown by Monet at Paul Durand-Ruel's gallery in Paris in May 1909. Titled *Les Nymphéas: Séries de Paysages d'Eau* (Waterlilies: Series of Waterscapes), the exhibition was met with adulation from Monet's ardent followers.

Monet started painting his waterlilies in the 1890s and over the course of thirty years painted them over three hundred times. An avid gardener, he cultivated the pond by his house in Giverny, Normandy. He imported exotic varieties and diverted water from the adjacent river to expand it. He employed a gardener to tend the pond, clear the weeds and dead foliage, and group the plants appropriately to create the visual effects Monet desired.

Gradually the waterlilies became an obsession. Since 1903 Monet had painted little else, apart from his views of Venice in 1908. He struggled against illness and worsening eyesight. At times despairing, he wrote 'They are beyond the powers of an old man, and yet I want to succeed in rendering what I feel'.

Focusing on effects of light and nature, Monet's works moved increasingly towards the intangible and purely visual, becoming almost abstract. This composition looks directly into the water, excluding his familiar Japanese bridge or any dry land or horizon. Only the lily flowers offer any solidity or perspective.

A number of works were sold before the exhibition. This one, no. 42, was lent by the artist but sold to Durand-Ruel soon after. In 1913 Gwendoline Davies purchased it in a set of three, for £3,370. They later hung as a group in the music room at Gregynog Hall, beautifully demonstrating the evocative effects of Monet's work in series. *AP*

89. Erich Heckel
(b. Döbeln, Germany 1883;
d. Radolfzell 1970)

Lake near Moritzburg
1909
Oil on canvas, 60.2 x 70.5cm
Purchased, 1973
NMW A 2053

Composed from blocks of intense, flat colour and bold expressive brushstrokes, this picture points to Heckel's awareness of the latest developments from Paris including Post-Impressionism and Fauvism. Heckel was one of the founding figures of the German Expressionist group known as Die Brücke (the Bridge). Like many avant-garde groups in Europe at this time, the group rejected traditional academic art in favour of 'authenticity' and 'directness'. Looking to so-called primitive societies in search for these qualities, they decorated their studios with tribal art and artefacts.

This rejection of Western society encouraged the group to spend the summers between 1909 and 1911 at the Moriztburg Lakes. It was here, away from the conservative confines of Dresden, that Die Brücke had greater opportunity to indulge in their bohemian lifestyle of communal living, bathing and sexual freedom. Their 'exotic primitivism' was influenced by Paul Gauguin, whose reputation was becoming established in Europe following his death in the Marquesas Islands in 1903. The flat colour, steep perspective and use of black outline all suggest that Heckel was looking at Gauguin's work when he painted this picture.

Along with the other founding members of Die Brücke – Ernst Ludwig Kirchner and Karl Schmidt-Rottluff – Heckel studied architecture at the Technical Academy in Dresden. Printmaking was also important to the Die Brücke artists; they looked to traditional techniques such as wood-cuts for their unsophisticated honesty. *Lake near Moritzburg*, with its flat colours and strong black outlines, corresponds in style to Heckel's own printmaking. *NT*

90. Natalia Goncharova
(b. Negayero, Tula Province,
Russia 1881; d. Paris, France 1962)

The Weaver
About 1913
Oil on canvas, 154.4 x 99.8cm
Purchased, 1975
NMW A 2056

This image of animated dynamism shows a weaver at an industrial loom, and is a key example of the short-lived but influential style of Rayonism developed by Goncharova and her partner Mikhail Larionov (1881-1964). Goncharova was a central figure of the pre-Revolution Russian avant-garde, painting Russian peasant life in a neo-primitive style that combined the influence of modern French painters with folk art and Byzantine icons.

The Rayonist manifesto described the Rayonist technique as 'spatial forms which are obtained through the crossing of rays from various objects'. *The Weaver* demonstrates this, but also shows the techniques of Futurism in the repetition of form to represent a trajectory, presented here with a juddering drive. As the electric light swings above the loom, the weaver's hands and feet become multiple, a representation of speed and skill.

Futurism glorified the machine, conveying dynamism and speed through paint. The Rayonist Manifesto likewise trumpeted the 'genius' of modern transportation mechanisms. At first glance *The Weaver*, which interestingly has also been known as *The Machine's Engine*, appears to promote this – yet Goncharova's engagement here is more circumspect. There is something distinctly oppressive about the cramped pictorial space, something precarious about the swinging light bulb and something threatening about the heavy iron structure. The diminutive figure in a traditional headscarf hunched over the loom is almost consumed as the mechanism races on – machine as industrial enslaver rather than liberator.

This tension between the urban and rural meant that Rayonism as a movement was short-lived, and Goncharova later settled in Paris where she became a celebrated designer for Diaghilev's *Ballets Russes*: the perfect fusion of Russian folk tradition and the avant-garde. *BD*

91. Wassily Kandinsky

(b. Moscow, Russia 1866;
d. Paris, France 1944)

Acid Green Crescent

1927

Watercolour, ink, bodycolour on paper,
48.2 x 32cm

Purchased with the assistance of the
Derek Williams Trust (Centenary Fund),
2007

NMW A 29231

Russian-born Wassily Kandinsky was
a pivotal figure in the development
of modern art, and one of the most
influential artists and theorists of the
twentieth century. In 1922 he accepted
a teaching post at the Bauhaus, first in
Weimar and then, following its relocation
in 1925, Dessau, where he painted this
picture. By this time Kandinsky had
abandoned the overt, vibrant drama of
his pre-war Expressionism, developing
instead a more refined mode of painting
using line and geometric form. This
reflected not just the prevailing Bauhaus
aesthetic of rationalism, but post-war
European currents generally; yet pure
objectivity was never Kandinsky's aim –
his interest remained in colour, feeling
and the emotional experience of art. In
1926 he had published *Point and Line
to Plane*, a treatise on the interaction of
colour, line and picture plane and the
subjective effect on the viewer. *Acid
Green Crescent* is an expression of this.

In 1937, the painting was confiscated
from a gallery in Halle by the National
Socialist Party, for display in the
infamous *Entartete Kunst* (Degenerate
Art) exhibition held in Munich in 1937.
Part of Hitler's use of cultural
propaganda to enforce Nazi ideology,
Entartete Kunst was designed to illustrate
to the German people, in the most
derisive terms, precisely what constituted
'un-German' art (most forms of modern
or progressive art). Many included artists
who fled Germany or were exiled –
Kandinsky himself had moved to Paris
following the Nazi's closure of the
Bauhaus (by then relocated to Berlin)
in 1933, becoming a French citizen just
before the outbreak of the Second World
War. *BD*

92. Max Ernst
(b. Bruhl, Germany 1891;
d. Paris, France 1976)

The Wood
1927

Oil on canvas, 60.5 x 81.5cm

Given by the Contemporary Art Society,
1991

NMW A 503

Max Ernst was haunted by the darkness and the enchantment of forests from childhood. *The Wood* is part of a major series of paintings where the forest is the main subject matter. The principal motif in this painting is the birds in the bottom half of the image. From an early age he identified with birds and he often introduced them as familiar spirits in his pictures.

The birds and the sun are the only areas of the picture that have been applied directly by paintbrush. The rest of the image has been achieved using a method invented by Ernst called *grattage*. This involved layering paint onto the canvas using a palette knife, laying on top a textured surface and then scraping off the paint, leaving chance marks and indentations.

Ernst was a member of the Paris Surrealist group, which formed in 1924. The Surrealist group was concerned with exploring the unconscious, dreams and fantasy. He was originally a member of Dada, an anarchist movement formed during the First World War, but became involved with Surrealism after moving to Paris in 1922. He fled the Nazis in 1941 and emigrated to the USA where he married the art collector Peggy Guggenheim.

The Wood is significant because of its early arrival in Britain. Ernst's work was first seen in London at the Mayor Gallery in 1933. The British Surrealist movement was not launched until 1936, and in 1938 a retrospective exhibition of Ernst's work was held in Britain as a benefit for Czech and Jewish refugees. *The Wood* was first lent to the Contemporary Art Society in 1938 and then given in 1940.
MM

93. René Magritte
(b. Lessines, Belgium 1898;
d. Brussels 1967)

Le Masque Vide (The Empty Mask)
1928
Oil on canvas, 81.2 x 116.2cm
Purchased, 1973
NMW A 2051

The Empty Mask is a contradictory title, as the mask is not empty. Magritte presents us with an irregularly shaped framed object with six compartments, each containing a picture. There is an image of the sky, a lead curtain with bells attached, a façade of a house, fire, forest and a paper cut-out. It would appear that these are portals into another world or reflections of Magritte's unconscious thoughts. Magritte plays with the viewer's perception of a real object and an image of the object. He also appears to be challenging the painterly tradition of using a rectangular format; the object is a gilt frame like a painting, but with gilding through the middle to divide it into sections. The challenge is contradicted by containing this image within a rectangular canvas.

This is the first of three versions of the *The Empty Mask*, all of which culminate in 1930's *On the Threshold of Freedom*

(Museum Boijmans-Van Beuningen, Rotterdam). In this work each scene is presented on a room panel and a canon is preparing to fire through the walls.

Magritte was a member of the Belgian Surrealist group, and worked closely with the Paris Surrealists from 1927 to 1930 when he was living and working in Paris. He returned to Brussels due to his difficult relationship with André Breton, the leader of the Surrealist group, and the global economic crisis. When Germany invaded Belgium in 1940, Magritte fled to the south of France. After the war his relationship with the Paris Surrealists did not improve and Breton expelled him from the group. However, Magritte continued showing his work in major international exhibitions until his death in 1967. *MM*

94. Pablo Picasso
(b. Málaga, Spain 1881;
d. Mougins, France 1973)

Still Life with Poron
1948
Oil on canvas, 50.3 x 61cm
Purchased with assistance of the
Derek Williams Trust (Centenary Fund)
and the Art Fund, 2009
NMW A 29458

This is one of three still-lifes Picasso painted on 26 December 1948. The ingredients for a meal – a lemon, a lobster and a *poron* (from porrón, a traditional Spanish wine pitcher) – have been placed on a table which is tipped towards the viewer. The table sits on a floor made from distinctive hexagonal tiles, which identifies the location as Picasso's studio on the Rue des Grands Augustins in Paris.

Picasso painted relatively few oil paintings in 1948. For much of this year he was based in Vallauris in the south of France focusing on the production of ceramics at the Madoura Pottery (see no. 95). When he did turn to painting, his chosen subjects were drawn from his immediate surroundings – his partner Françoise Gilot, their young son Claude and still life.

Picasso's adoption of a softer, less rigorous Cubist style for this work is typical of his still-life painting at this time. However, the inclusion of the *porrón* suggests a more charged and complex work. Picasso first painted the vessel in 1906 during an extended visit to Gósol in Spain. John Richardson has interpreted the *porrón* in these early paintings as phallic puns, stating that they anticipate the sexual metaphors of his later still-lifes.

Picasso is arguably the single most important and influential artist of the twentieth century. His development of Cubism radically changed the direction of modern art. This is the first Picasso oil painting to enter a public collection in Wales. The acquisition was made possible through the creation of a special fund supported by the Derek Williams Trust to celebrate the Museum's centenary. *NT*

95. Pablo Picasso
(b. Málaga, Spain 1881;
d. Mougins, France 1973)

Zoomorphic vase, 'La Tarasque'
Unique ceramic, 1954

Tin-glazed earthenware, painted in slips and incised. Made and decorated at the Madoura Pottery, Vallauris

Height 35.5cm

Purchased with the assistance of the Derek Williams Trust (Centenary Fund), 2008

NMW A 39003

In this appealingly zoomorphic form, Picasso plays a double game of metamorphosis. The first transformation is that of a jug or vase into the form of a dove. He has then reinterpreted this so that the neck becomes a turret filled with nervous soldiers and the body becomes the Tarasque monster. A version of the monster is painted and incised on the dove's breast but, most surprisingly and amusingly, when turned round the jug reveals that the bird's tail has become the monster's head and the handle the ridge of its spine.

The Tarasque was a legendary dragon-like creature with a lion's head. It terrorised the area around Nerluc in Provence until Saint Martha tamed it with hymns, prayers and holy water. She led the unresisting creature back to the city, whose traumatised people attacked and killed the helpless monster but then showed repentance by changing their town's name to Tarascon. The annual Tarasque procession in Tarascon features a monster whose form probably inspired Picasso.

Picasso first studied ceramics in Paris at the beginning of the twentieth century, but only took to it seriously after visiting Suzanne and Georges Ramié's Madoura pottery at Vallauris in the south of France in July 1946. Thereafter he returned every year, making nearly 4,000 objects in a period of some twenty years.

Picasso's work in clay is perhaps the most overlooked aspect of his artistic oeuvre, but one that nonetheless demonstrates the same extraordinary vitality and creativity that is found in his paintings, sculpture, prints and drawings. His love of tradition, uninhibited originality and typically mischievous sense of humour helped to redefine the potential of ceramics as an art form. *AR*

96. Maurice Marinot
(b. Troyes, France 1882;
d. Troyes 1960)

Bottles
1929-30
Glass, maximum height: 16.3cm
Given by Mlle Florence Marinot, 1973
NMW A 50737, 50742, 50744

Maurice Marinot was a pioneer in the development of glass as a studio art form. He began his career as a painter, one of the Fauves ('wild beasts') of French art, whose bold use of pure colour earned them the nickname.

Marinot discovered glass in 1911 when he visited the glass works of the Viard brothers at Bar-sur-Seine and was immediately captivated. He initially drew on his skill as a painter, decorating simple glass shapes made for him with striking, brightly coloured enamels. After a long, self-imposed apprenticeship he began to create his own highly experimental glass forms.

Marinot made unique pieces, using hand-methods and without the use of moulds. Using the full range of glassmaking skills, he blew and worked the hot glass, acid-etched and wheel-cut it when cold. He encased coloured glass within clear glass like geological strata. He created the effect of cracked ice by plunging hot glass into cold water, or the suggestion of moving water by the careful control of air bubbles.

To Marinot, glass was a muscular, expressive material and he enjoyed the physical challenges of working with it. He rejected the label of decorative art, preferring to consider his glass as sculpture and insisting it was free from the constraints of functionality. A combination of failing health and the closure of the Viard's works in 1937 caused Marinot to stop making glass and he returned to painting and drawing.

In 1973 Marinot's daughter Florence gave a group of twenty pieces of glass to the Museum. The gift also included four oil paintings and 101 drawings, including designs for glass. *RC*

97. Harold Gilman
(b. Rode, Somerset 1876;
d. London 1919)

The Kitchen
1908-09
Oil on canvas, 62 x 46.2cm
Given by the Contemporary Art Society
for Wales, 1957
NMW A 191

This scene was probably painted at 15 Westholme Green, Letchworth, where the artist lived with his family in 1908-09. The painting has the sense of catching a fleeting glimpse into a private, intimate world. The composition plays with our sense of interior space. The open door draws the eye towards the solitary figure, yet the door frame and abbreviated picture frames mark out the intervening wall, signalling the boundary between artist and subject.

Gilman admired seventeenth-century Dutch painting, in which there was a revival of interest around 1900. Servants depicted in domestic interiors are a routine subject in Dutch genre painting. His acute observation of the light, shining through the thin curtains, gleaming on the door and reflecting off the clean crockery and door handle, suggests the influence of Johannes Vermeer (1632-1675). The softly graduated cream and gold tones also reflect the ideas of Whistler (1834-1903) (see no. 67).

Gilman met Walter Sickert (1860-1942) in 1907 and later that year became a founder member of the Fitzroy Street group, an association of artists who met at 19 Fitzroy Street, London, to discuss and exhibit their paintings. The group believed in painting scenes of everyday life; in 1910 Sickert declared that 'serious art' found its subject matter in the scullery or the kitchen, shunning the drawing room and polite society.

Gilman trained in Hastings and at the Slade School of Fine Art in London from 1897-1901. He became one of the most accomplished British exponents of Post-Impressionism and a member of the Camden Town Group, founded in 1911. He died of influenza, aged forty-three.
CT

98. Gwen John

(b. Haverfordwest, Pembrokeshire 1876;
d. Dieppe, France 1939)

A Corner of the Artist's Room
1907-09
Oil on canvas on board, 31.2 x 24.8cm
Purchased with the assistance of the
Derek Williams Trust and the Estate of
Mrs J. Green, 1995
NMW A 3397

This is the attic of 87 rue du Cherche-Midi, Paris where Gwen John lived between 1907 and 1909. It is a moment captured in time; the book on the table is open, the window ajar and the coat thrown over the wicker chair. Sun floods in from the open window, drawing the eye beyond the room to the world outside. The artist seems present even though unseen. John was very proud of her surroundings, writing, 'I must tell you ... what a feeling of contentment my room gives me. I take my meals at the table in the window ... In the evening my room gives me a quite extraordinary feeling of pleasure.'

This is one of a group of interiors that John painted during this period, repeatedly using her personal possessions. Although it can be compared to works by her contemporaries, this is not the busy, domestic room of a bourgeois family, but a plain room, a working room for a serious artist, as well as a living space. The contemplative atmosphere shows the influence of seventeenth-century Dutch genre paintings. She may also have been familiar with the sparse interiors of the contemporary Danish artist Vilhem Hammershøi (1864-1916).

In 1895 Gwen John followed her younger, flamboyant brother Augustus (1878-1961) to study at the Slade School of Fine Art in London. In 1904 she moved to Paris, where she made a living as a model and began a passionate affair with Auguste Rodin (1840-1917). Interiors are a central subject in her oil paintings. The subject she painted most often, however, was three-quarter length portraits of female figures, several of which are also in the Museum's collection. *BM*

99. Gwen John
(b. Haverfordwest, Pembrokeshire 1876;
d. Dieppe, France 1939)

Nuns and Schoolchildren in Church
Watercolour and bodycolour on paper,
16.8 x 12.5cm
Purchased, 1976
NMW A 3614

The nun here was a member of the Meudon Chapter of the Order of the Sisters of Charity of the Holy Virgin of Tours. Gwen John moved to the Paris suburb of Meudon in 1911 and began instruction in the Roman Catholic Church there, converting probably in early 1913.

This composition began as a drawing. She wrote, 'I am in love with the atmosphere of Meudon church and the people who go to church here have a charm for me'. One of her neighbours recalled, 'I saw coming into the church a woman with a felt hat with a wide brim, dressed in a long cape, who slid discreetly to the end of the church, and there, without kneeling like the other worshippers, pulled out a sketchbook and began to draw'. Gwen drew during services, making hundreds of sketches in charcoal, particularly of the nuns and

orphans from the Meudon Chapter. Many of them are drawn from behind. She would work up the drawings back in her studio, adding watercolour and repeating and simplifying compositions. She responded to a criticism for working in church with, 'I like to pray in Church like everyone but my spirit is not capable of praying for a long time at once – if I remove all that time there would not be enough happiness in my life'.

The Museum has an unrivalled collection of Gwen John's works. After her death her nephew Edwin John inherited her estate and found her paintings stacked up and a 'mass of beautiful drawings'. The Museum acquired over nine hundred works in 1976. Many are unfinished studies or rapid sketches, that give a unique insight into Gwen's working methods and subjects. *BM*

100. Augustus John
(b. Tenby, Pembrokeshire 1878;
d. Fordingbridge, Hampshire 1961)

Pyramus John
About 1908
Pencil on paper, 35.5 x 25.2cm
Bequeathed by Gwendoline Davies, 1951
NMW A 3225

Pyramus was the eldest child of John and Dorelia McNeill (1881-1969) (see no. 101), who gave birth to him alone in a caravan on Dartmoor. He was a strikingly handsome child and was greatly loved by the family. In the same year as making this drawing John wrote 'Pyramus grows more lyrically beautiful every day. He is like a little divine phrase from Shelley or Wordsworth'. Here his direct, wide-eyed gaze gives a sense of immediacy and innocence, a fleeting expression captured in pencil.

Pyramus died of meningitis at the age of seven, a few days after the birth of his sister Poppet in March 1912. As he lay dying his father wrote 'he was indeed a celestial child and that is why the Gods take him'.

From his student days at the Slade School of Fine Art in London, John was renowned for the boldness and fluency of his drawings. It was said that other students would retrieve his discarded sketches from the wastepaper basket, such was his technical virtuosity. The Slade emphasised skill in figure drawing, and students were taught to make numerous rapid sketches from life and to copy drawing techniques from Old Master prints and drawings in the British Museum. The parallel hatching used here to catch the fall of light on the face is characteristic of the Slade style.

John's immediate family were among his favourite models. After his wife Ida died in March 1907, John seems to have drawn and painted his six sons and Dorelia with even greater frequency and intensity. This work became the basis for a posthumous oil portrait, also in the Museum's collection (see left). *CT*

101. Augustus John
(b. Tenby, Pembrokeshire 1878;
d. Fordingbridge, Hampshire 1961)

Dorelia McNeill in the Garden at Alderney Manor
1911

Oil on canvas, 201 x 101.6cm
Purchased with the assistance of the Knapping Fund, 1962
NMW A 163

This larger-than-life portrait, with its exaggerated perspective, shows the influence of Post-Impressionism on John's work. Bright, flat areas of colour give a decorative, patterning effect, recalling the work of the Fauves ('wild beasts') of the French avant-garde. Sharp contours and Dorelia's bold stance suggest the influence of Paul Gauguin (1848-1903), whom John admired. A second ghostly pair of eyes looms from Dorelia's cheeks, as the ageing surface paint layers reveal alterations to the composition. Although John is sometimes now regarded as a reactionary figure, this portrait reflects how the artist was regarded when it was painted – as the leading modern artist. 'After Picasso,' wrote one critic, 'Mr John'.

The John household moved to Alderney Manor, Dorset, in August 1911. Dorelia's son Romilly later recalled 'As soon as we were established at Alderney, Dorelia, who had a passion for flowers, began to make something of the walled garden which … began very shortly to look exquisite'. The garden with its 'half-wild appearance' and swarming bees and butterflies 'became an enchanted place', particularly evocative of Dorelia's personality. This triumphal portrait celebrates the family's new home, where the Johns lived until 1927.

John married a Slade School contemporary, Ida Nettleship (1877-1907), in 1901. Two years later he met Dorelia McNeill (1881-1969), a friend of his sister Gwen's. Dorelia became his mistress, part of a ménage-a-trois that endured until Ida's early death in 1907. Dorelia's hypnotic beauty and her serenity captivated John for the next sixty years. Her enigmatic quality, manifest in John's many portraits of her, inspired and liberated John to paint her in many different guises. *CT*

102. James Dickson Innes
(b. Llanelli, Carmarthenshire 1887;
d. Swanley, Kent 1914)

Arenig
About 1911-12
Oil on panel, 23 x 33cm
Given by Sir Edward Marsh, 1954
NMW A 202

Innes discovered Arenig, near Bala, during a tour of north Wales in 1910. The mountain became his focal point and 'his spiritual home'. He painted it repeatedly, responding to changing weather conditions, seeking the moment of revelation to be found in some transitory, glorious light effect.

In 1911 Innes travelled to Arenig with Augustus John. They rented a cottage at Nant-ddu, near Rhyd-y-fen. Their relationship was mutually beneficial; John was inspired by Innes's vision and intensity. Under John's influence, Innes began to paint in oil on small wooden panels, using short strokes of brilliant colour, a technique John developed while working in Provence in 1910. Innes's rapid, expressive brushstrokes are clearly visible in this work. The flat, simplified composition is probably derived from Japanese prints. The paintings produced by Innes and John in Wales over the next three years represent a unique, Welsh, contribution to British Post-Impressionism.

Innes studied at Carmarthen School of Art and at the Slade School of Fine Art, where he was taught by Philip Wilson Steer (1860-1942). His first visit to France in 1908 transformed his awareness of colour. Diagnosed with tuberculosis in 1909, he worked at a furious pace. His illness did not prevent him, however, from leading an itinerant, bohemian existence. He travelled continually, painting most frequently in Wales and at Collioure, the French coastal town associated with the Fauves Henri Matisse (1869-1954) and André Derain (1880-1954).

Innes died aged 27. John later wrote 'tortured by the remorseless disease … he managed by heroic effort to make a name for himself as one of the foremost figures of his time in the art of landscape painting'. *CT*

103. Sir George Clausen
(b. London 1852;
d. Newbury, Berkshire 1944)

In the Fields in June
1914
Oil on canvas, 183 x 213.7cm
Purchased, 1914
NMW A 176

Rural scenes were a favourite subject for Clausen, and his paintings often show peasants in a landscape. He admired Jean François Millet (1814-1875), famous for his paintings of French rural life, writing 'No other has seen so clearly or shown so well the beauty and significance of ordinary occupations, the union of man with nature.'

Clausen was familiar with the French Impressionists, having studied in Antwerp and Paris. Like them he was fascinated by the effects of light. Here, the light falls from the top left of the painting, casting the facial features of the standing man into shadow. The horizon is low, silhouetting all three figures against the sky and adding a sense of monumentality.

This work was exhibited at the Royal Academy in 1914 where representatives of the Museum saw it, and purchased it later the same year. Before sending the picture to Cardiff, Clausen wrote, '...there are some things I want to do to it yet – some work on the sky which I could not judge properly till I saw it in the RA. Now that it is going into your museum, I want to leave it, so far as I can, without faults.' He reworked some of it, particularly the sky, where he added to the diagonal effect of the clouds.

Clausen, whose father was Danish, was regarded in late Victorian London as an artistic radical and a champion of continental methods. He was a founder-member of the New English Art Club in 1886. After his election as associate of the Royal Academy in 1895 he taught at the Royal Academy Schools. A friend of the sculptor William Goscombe John, he also judged and selected at exhibitions in Wales. *BM*

104. Dame Laura Knight
(b. Long Eaton, Derby 1877;
d. London 1970)

The Cornish Coast
1914-17
Oil on canvas, 64.8 x 76.3cm
Bequeathed by F. H. Lambert, 1940
NMW A 3706

The poses of these two women suggest independence and liberty. Set on the brink between land and sea, they gaze into the distance, released from the confines of the domestic sphere. Their bright clothes contrast with the muted tones of earth and sky. The standing girl is Phyllis Vipond-Crocker (1900-1938) from Penzance, who modelled for several of the Newlyn artists. The artist's dog, Tip, is asleep in the foreground.

Laura Knight moved to Newlyn, in west Cornwall, with her husband the painter Harold Knight (1874-1961) in 1907. Newlyn was a thriving artistic centre, based around the School of Painting founded by Stanhope Forbes in 1899. The Knights soon became part of a dynamic social and artistic group. A fellow artist, Norman Garstin (1847-1926), recalled 'there came over their work an utter change in both their outlook and method: they at once plunged into a riot of brilliant sunshine, of opulent colour and of sensuous gaiety'.

The clear Cornish light and the dramatic coastal scenery transformed Knight's work. Monochrome tones and interior subjects were replaced by bright colour, vigorous brushwork and a new commitment to painting outdoors. She could often be seen struggling up precipitous cliff paths balancing six foot canvases on her head. She painted numerous scenes of female figures in landscape.

Knight became a noted painter of theatre, ballet and gypsy scenes. She was the first woman to be elected a full member of the Royal Academy in 1936. As a commissioned war artist, she produced one of the iconic images of women in wartime, *Ruby Loftus screwing a Breech-Ring* (Imperial War Museum), painted at a munitions factory in Newport, Gwent in 1943. *CT*

105. Sir Jacob Epstein
(b. New York, USA 1880;
d. London 1959)

Rom
1910
Limestone, height: 85cm; width: 31cm;
depth: 31cm
Purchased, 1979
NMW A 2532

This is the head of Romilly John (1906-1986), the second child of Augustus John and Dorelia McNeill (see no. 101). It is based on an earlier bronze sculpture commissioned by Augustus John in 1907. At the time Epstein carved *Rom* he was working closely with the sculptor Eric Gill (see no. 106), who used his skill as a letter cutter to carve the inscription on the base.

Rom is an early and important example of Epstein carving directly in stone. Along with other avant-garde sculptors working in Europe at this time, Epstein became an enthusiastic exponent of direct carving and the belief that a sculpture should emerge through an artist's engagement with the chosen material.

Epstein's conversion to direct carving was in part inspired by his admiration for the ancient and non-Western sculpture that he saw on visits to the Louvre and the British Museum. The vitality of these 'primitive' forms was an important influence on avant-garde sculptors at this time. The rough-hewn carving of *Rom*, the stylised details such as the incised hair and the way the head emerges so directly from the block all point to Epstein's enthusiasm for non-Western sculpture.

It is likely that *Rom* was conceived for an ambitious temple planned by Epstein and Gill for the Sussex Downs. Gill described the project as a 'sort of twentieth-century stonehenge'. Although the temple was never realized the pagan associations were picked up by C. Lewis Hind when he remarked in his book *The Post Impressionists* (1911) that *Rom* was made as 'one of the flanking figures of a group apotheosising Man and Woman, around a central shrine, that the sculptor destines in his dreams for a great temple'.
NT

© The artist's estate

106. Eric Gill
(b. Brighton 1882;
d. Uxbridge, Middlesex 1940)

Mother and Child
1910

Portland stone, height: 61.5cm;
width: 21.1cm; depth: 17.5cm

Purchased, 1983

NMW A 312

This carving was made while Gill was living at Sopers in Ditchling, Sussex. Here he founded an artist colony called The Guild of St Joseph and St Dominic to practice crafts including wood-engraving, calligraphy and stone carving. Gill was an early British exponent of direct carving, in which artists worked directly from the block, favouring simple forms through which the qualities of the material could be exposed. He felt that 'stone carvings are not only born but conceived in stone, they are of stone in their inmost being as well as their outermost existence.' Although he claimed no external influence for the forms he created, his work recalls the simplicity of medieval ecclesiastical and Byzantine sculpture.

Mother and Child is one of Gill's earliest stone figure carvings; although he was trained as a stonemason, his stone work up until 1910 had been entirely letter-based. He was moved by the third pregnancy of his wife, Ethel Mary, to create a group of mother and child figures. Although this carving is probably a response to the birth of his daughter Joanna, the child is in fact male, which lends a distinct overtone of Christianity – Gill converted to Catholicism in 1913, and his religion became an overriding force. Roger Fry later wrote of this piece in a letter to Clive Bell 'has anyone ever looked at the real thing and seen its pathetic animalism as Gill has? Merely to have seen what the gesture of the pressing of the breast with the left hand means, as he has, seems to be a piece of deep imagination.'

Gill settled at Capel-y-ffin in the Black Mountains between 1924 and 1928 (see no. 111). *BD*

107. Henri Gaudier-Brzeska
(b. Orléans, France 1891;
d. Neuville-Sant-Vaast 1915)

Men with Bowl
1914 (later cast)

Bronze, height: 30.6cm; width: 25.6cm;
depth: 15.6cm

Purchased, 1992

NMW A 1625

Men with Bowl was made as a study for
a garden ornament or bird bath. It was
originally modelled in plaster in 1914.
This bronze is one of an edition of four,
a posthumous cast probably dating from
the late 1920s or 1930s. The surface has
a faceted, rough-hewn quality giving it
an almost carved appearance.

Although Gaudier-Brzeska modelled in
clay and plaster, a visit to Epstein's studio
in 1912 converted him to direct carving
in stone (see no. 105). He also admired
ancient and non-Western sculpture and
made regular visits to the ethnographic
collections at the British Museum. The
primitive appearance of *Men with Bowl*
suggests the influence of both African
and Polynesian sculpture. He described it
as 'a study of the primitive so that I may
carve stone with more purpose'.

Gaudier-Brzeska visited Britain in 1907
on a language and business scholarship.
Between September 1908 and April 1909
he worked for the Cardiff coal exporters
Fifoot & Ching, taking lodgings on
Claude Road in Roath. During this
period he made numerous sketches in
Cardiff, taking inspiration from the
docks, Victoria Park, Llandaff Cathedral
and the city's municipal museum. His
employer Mr Ching later recalled,
'During his lunch hours he periodically
walked across to the docks and brought
back with him a small sketch of, perhaps,
the bow of a boat, or the elevation of a
crane or tip, all of which showed genius.'

In the following years Gaudier-Brzeska
focused on sculpture and soon emerged
as a leading modern sculptor. In 1915
his career was tragically cut short when,
after joining the French army, he was
killed in action. *NT*

108. Bernard Leach
(b. Hong Kong 1887;
d. St Ives, Cornwall 1979)

Jar
1923
Lead-glazed earthenware with
incised slip decoration
Height: 18.6cm
Purchased from the artist, 1924
NMW A 32116

Michael Cardew
(b. Wimbledon, Surry 1901
d. Truro, Cornwall 1983)

Jar
About 1928-30
Lead-glazed earthenware with
brushed slip decoration
Height: 36.8cm
Purchased, 2001
NMW A 36130

Writing in January 1924 to his uncle
Dr William Evans Hoyle, then the
National Museum's first Director,
Bernard Leach described this jar as 'the
best pot of the same [slip] ware which I
have made in England'. The tree motif
on each side was a Leach favourite. The
mottling of the ground was probably
done with the wrong end of a bamboo-
handled brush. While Leach described the
pot itself as 'English slip ware', the style
of decoration echoes a Chinese Song-
dynasty Cizhou stoneware vase that
Leach admired.

Although Leach struggled to make
a living in the 1920s and 1930s, he
went on to become the century's most
influential potter. Through his pots, his
writing and his eloquent proselytising he
inspired generations of potters to imitate
his Orientalising manner. While he
considered East Asian – and particularly
Song-dynasty Chinese – pottery to be
'the noblest achievement in ceramics',
in seventeenth-century English slipware

he found an authentic indigenous
counterpart worthy of emulation.

The great champion of slipware was,
however, Michael Cardew, the most
important of Leach's students. Childhood
experience of traditional North Devon
slipware fired Cardew's passion to revive
this fast-disappearing folk art. After three
years working at Leach's pottery (1923-
1926), and by virtue of great personal
hardship and idealistic commitment,
Cardew succeeded in re-establishing the
traditional pottery at Winchcombe in
Gloucestershire.

Boldly thrown and decorated, this
storage jar embodies Cardew's growing
confidence as an artist-potter. The
painting shows the influence of Chinese
Cizhou stoneware and may well have
been executed using one of the three
Japanese 'Sen Pen Banka' brushes given
to him by Leach when he left the St Ives
Pottery in 1926. *AR*

109. Percy Wyndham Lewis

(b. Nova Scotia, Canada 1882;
d. London 1957)

Ezra Pound (1885-1972)
1919

Pencil, watercolour and bodycolour
on wove paper, 35.5 x 38.5cm

Bequeathed by Margaret Davies, 1963

NMW A 1867

Ezra Pound, poet, critic and Modernist, appears here like a living sculpture. Firm rhythmic lines describe his bone structure, while brown wash, softly graduated, fills out the contours of his face. A single outline sweep of colour, a device often used by Lewis, accentuates the volumetric dome of Pound's head.

This drawing is one of several made in 1919 as part of preparations for a major, larger-than-life oil portrait, now lost or destroyed by the artist. It was made the year before Pound left London for Paris, disappointed by the sluggishness of avant-garde development in Britain. Pound is shown lying back, seemingly absorbed in thought. This attitude may have been particularly characteristic of the sitter, as Lewis used a similar pose for a portrait of Pound painted twenty years later (Tate).

Lewis and Pound became closely associated in 1913, when they joined forces as the main theorists and advocates of Vorticism. The Vorticist movement, a name coined by Pound, was conceived as a British alternative to Cubism and Futurism, an art to match the dynamism of the modern age. In July 1914 Lewis and Pound collaborated over the magazine *Blast*, setting out the Vorticist manifesto to 'produce a New Living Abstraction'. The geometric arcs and angles of this work are derived from a Vorticist style, though by 1919 Lewis's work was becoming more figurative.

Lewis produced numerous portraits of well-known personalities during the 1920s and 1930s. In 1932, the artist Walter Sickert (1860-1942) wrote 'Wyndham Lewis [is] the greatest portraitist of this or any other time'. *CT*

110. Sir Frank Brangwyn
(b. Bruges, Belgium 1867;
d. Ditchling, Sussex 1956)

A Tank in Action
1926-8
Oil on canvas, 366 x 376cm
Given by the artist, 1931
NMW A 2531

The advancing soldiers in the foreground are life-size, and behind them looms a British tank of the First World War, with a long-barrelled six-pounder gun protruding aggressively from its side. This was the word's first combat tank, developed to break through the trenches of the Western Front.

This picture and its pair, *A Big Gun in Action*, were conceived as part of a series of murals to cover the north and south walls of the royal gallery in the House of Lords. The Lords had decided in 1924 that there should be a memorial to peers and their relatives who had died in the War. Lord Iveagh offered to pay for the work and in 1926 he gave Brangwyn the commission.

After Brangwyn had worked for two years, Lord Iveagh could not accept the grim realities depicted and asked him to start afresh on a different scheme. The new series, in brilliant colours, evoked instead the beauty of the British dominions and colonies. The resulting *British Empire Panels* are a celebration of their people, flora and fauna. These proved too exuberant for the Lords, and in 1934 they were bought by the Corporation of Swansea and installed in the Guildhall.

Although Brangwyn was largely self-taught, he rapidly became one of the most celebrated and prolific British artists of the early twentieth century. His work ranged from vast mural paintings to watercolours, prints and designs as well as book illustrations and posters. Proud of his Welsh ancestry, the panels are part of a group of gifts he made to the National Museum in 1929-1935. Insistent that they were not gallery pictures, he agreed the locations in the Museum's Main Hall, where they have been ever since. *OF*

111. David Jones
(b. Brockley, Kent 1895;
d. Harrow-on-the-Hill, London 1974)

Capel-y-ffin
1926-7
Pen, watercolour and bodycolour on
paper, 56.2 x 38.9cm
Purchased, 1991
NMW A 557

Jones first came to Capel-y-ffin, near Llanthony in the Black Mountains, in 1924 to join Eric Gill's community based in the former monastery buildings (upper left here). Jones was then engaged to Gill's daughter Petra and he visited regularly, staying for long periods, over the next four years. He gave this watercolour to the Gill family as a Christmas present in 1927.

Jones found the Welsh hills a liberating subject. He wrote of 'the impact of the strong hill-rhythms and the bright counter-rhythms of "afonydd dyfroedd" (water-brooks)'. He produced numerous views of the surrounding area, especially Y Twmpa, the great hill across the valley.

He saw the Welsh border landscape as imbued with historic and mythological significance. The grazing ponies here may refer to the end of Arthurian Britain, when the horses of the knights of the Round Table ran free: 'Those straying riderless horses gone to grass in forest and on mountain ... We seem to have seen their descendants, shrunken in bulk ... but holding themselves with breeding, black in colour, and primitive in contour on a Brecon hill-slope'. The strong, formal pattern of this work also shows the influence of Paul Cézanne's landscapes.

During the First World War Jones served on the Western Front, an experience that coloured the rest of his life. It found expression in the epic poem *In Parenthesis* (1937). He converted to Roman Catholicism in 1921 and joined Gill's community, the Guild of St Joseph and St Dominic, in Ditchling, Sussex. Jones is now recognized as one of the most original figures of the modernist movement, and there are over 250 of his works in the Museum's collection. *CT*

112. Paul Nash
(b. London 1889;
d. Boscombe, Dorset 1946)

Plage
1928
Oil on canvas, 72.8 x 49.5cm
Purchased, 1992
NMW A 1663

This giant fountain provides a juxtaposition of natural elements – freshwater against sea water. In his 1980 monograph on the artist Andrew Causey suggested that the fountain is symbolic of the purity of the Virgin Mary set against the roughness of the sea. It was not uncommon for Paul Nash to imbue inanimate objects with a sense of life and character.

The picture was exhibited with the above title at the Leicester Galleries in 1929. By the mid-1930s it was also called *Moorish Tower* or *the Moorish Tower, Cros de Cagnes*. Nash stayed at the Pension de la Plage in Cros de Cagnes, near Nice, in January 1925. He saw 1928 as the year of 'a new vision and a new style'. The next ten years were for him an experimental phase. He was aware of the European Surrealists and drew on their innovations to revitalise his work.

Nash studied at the Slade School of Art in London where he met and became friends with St Ives artist Ben Nicholson (1894-1982) (see no. 116). Although throughout his career he bore a great affiliation to nature and the landscape, he is most well known for his drawings of the trenches at Ypres Salient, where he was posted in 1917. After visiting Paris in the 1920s he began working in a surrealist style. He was a member of the short-lived Unit One group – a group of English artists working in an avant-garde manner. In 1936 he was selected to sit on the committee for the organization of the International Surrealist Exhibition in London. *MM*

113. Evan Walters
(b. Llangyfelach, Glamorgan 1893;
d. London 1951)

The Communist, a political meeting
Around 1932
Oil on canvas, 76 x 92.1cm
Bequeathed by the artist, 1951
NMW A 2226

The politician's bright red waistcoat picks him out from the crowd and gives the viewer a visual clue to his politics. The painting's composition suggests a detachment between the speaker and his audience, a detachment accentuated by the Christ-like pose of the speaker. Are we meant to identify with speaker or the miners? As the art historian Peter Lord has remarked, there is little in Walters's written comments to resolve the political ambiguity of this painting.

Evan Walters was born in Llangyfelach, a mining village near Swansea. He left school at thirteen to work as a painter and decorator. After attending evening classes at Swansea School of Art he became a full-time student in 1911. Three years later he attended the Royal Academy Schools in London. His first solo exhibition at the Glynn Vivian

Gallery in 1920 was a critical success and helped secure his growing reputation in Wales. He enjoyed success as a portrait painter but his working-class background gave him the subject-matter for much of his art. The western coalfield – its workers and pitheads – were painted in a robust, realist style that was well placed to capture the hardship suffered by these communities in the 1920s and 1930s.

In 1935 Walters embarked on a radical change of style. His palette lightened and he developed a style based on his theory of 'double-vision'. This experimental style was unsuitable for representing industrial subjects of south Wales and may have contributed to his subsequent decline in popularity. This picture entered the Museum's collection through a bequest from the artist's estate of works left in the studio following Walter's death. *NT*

114. Sir Stanley Spencer

(b. Cookham, Berkshire 1891; d. Cliveden, Buckinghamshire 1959)

Souvenir of Switzerland
1934

Oil on three canvases, left panel: 106.5 x 76.5cm; middle panel: 107 x 168cm; right panel: 107 x 76cm

Purchased with the assistance of the Art Fund, the Heritage Lottery Fund and the Derek Williams Trust, 1998

NMW A 11709

This epic depiction of the life and inhabitants of Saas Fee, high in the Swiss Alps, was commissioned by the economist and patron Sir Edward Beddington-Behrens (1897-1968). In 1933 he invited Spencer to Switzerland, suggesting he might find inspiration in a place where religion was such an intrinsic part of everyday life. According to Spencer, 'Behrens sent a telegram saying "Come to the mountains nothing required, except strong boots & the spirit of adventure." So I went...' Spencer quickly became absorbed in what he described as 'the mixture of the religious life with the temporal life' – a phrase that aptly describes the content of much of his own painting. He was particularly taken by highly decorated wayside shrines and traditional costume: there are numerous examples here of regional dress, from the workaday white floral headdress to the

highly-embroidered black Sunday headwear and its white counterpart, worn specifically at christenings. The painting is made up of three panels. The use of multiple perspectives enabled Spencer to include a variety of unconnected groups. In among the throng, at the rear of the group to the right of the central panel, are two figures in contemporary dress: the male figure is Spencer himself and the female behind is probably Patricia Preece, with whom he was then infatuated.

Spencer did not begin the painting until his return to England, observing that 'if I feel it sufficiently intensely to paint from memory, it has got to live.' It met with a cool reception from Beddington-Behrens, who had anticipated a more naturalistic, and perhaps less rapturous, response to the landscape. *BD*

115. Sir Cedric Morris
(b. Sketty, Swansea 1889;
d. Ipswich, Suffolk 1982)

Two Sisters
1935
Oil on canvas, 76 x 63.5cm
Purchased with assistance of the
Derek Williams Trust, 2007
NMW A 29292

The subjects of this haunting portrait are Frances Byng-Stamper (left) and her sister Caroline Lucas. It was painted when Cedric Morris was trying to get together an exhibition of contemporary Welsh art. Frances, who lived at Manorbier Castle in Pembrokeshire, was the exhibition's secretary. Morris was himself an upper middle-class bohemian, but his relations with the mostly wealthy and anglicised members of the exhibition committee were edgy, and he gave this work the alternative title of 'The English Upper Classes'.

Today Morris is best remembered for his flower paintings, but his portraits are perhaps his most distinctive and radical achievement. While not caricatures, they often simplify and sometimes exaggerate the features to intensify the psychological impact. They owe more to French and German art of the 1910s and 1920s than to British painting, and they provoked strong reactions. The sisters rejected this painting, and the opening of an exhibition of Morris's portraits in 1938 degenerated into a brawl.

For all Morris's antipathy to the sisters, they were significant figures in the mid-century British art world. Frances was a long-term committee member of the Contemporary Art Society for Wales (which developed out of the 1935 exhibition). Caroline was a painter, sculptor and printmaker. Frances left Manorbier in 1939, and moved with her sister to Lewes in Sussex. There they established the Miller's Gallery, showing the work of Matisse, Roualt and Duncan Grant as well as Lucas's own. The sisters founded the Miller's Press in 1945 to encourage artists to work in colour lithography, and commissioned prints by a number of artists including Vanessa Bell, David Jones, Robert Colquhoun and Robert MacBryde. *OF*

116. Ben Nicholson
(b. Denham, Buckinghamshire 1894;
d. Hampstead, London 1982)

1940 – 43 (two forms)
1940-43
Oil on canvas on board, 60.5 x 59.5cm
Purchased, 1975
NMW A 2036

This work was made in St Ives, Cornwall, where Nicholson and his second wife Barbara Hepworth (1903-1975) (see no. 122) had relocated at the outbreak of war. In the decade before Nicholson had evolved a strict method of abstract art. He and Hepworth had met the Dutch artist Piet Mondrian (1872-1944) and other abstract artists in Paris and London. Nicholson explored the way a painting could create a sense of space and balance by using geometric forms and flat colours applied meticulously. At its most extreme, he made a group of white reliefs, which instead of colour used cut out forms on the surface resulting in actual light and shade.

Nicholson's earliest work was landscape and still life. Over the dark wartime period in Cornwall, there was a sense of him returning to these idioms. The size of his completed paintings reduced as materials became harder to acquire. The visual juxtapositions that still life and landscape created gradually informed his abstract compositions. He began to depart from pure abstraction. The rectangles and colours in many works gradually became more suggestive of forms such as cups and jugs on a table top.

This work, then, is on the cusp of this transition. The two forms of the title are composed of two groups of smaller rectangles. These cluster onto a background which is divided by a single horizontal in the foreground and a space whose dark tone suggests depth. Nicholson's play with colour and the illusion of spaces in juxtaposition includes a light rectangle on the right that may be read as either cut-out or pasted on. *MT*

117. John Piper
(b. Epsom 1903;
d. Henley-on-Thames 1992)

Grongar Hill
1938
Collage and ink on paper, 40.7. x 53cm
Purchased, 1978
NMW A 1874

This collage unites Piper's intellectual commitment to abstraction with his passion for landscape and history. Scraps of coloured paper are overlaid to form the contours of the hill. Rough torn black shapes suggest the racing clouds, while heavy ink lines show the hillside chequered with fields.

Grongar Hill lies near the River Towy, to the south-west of Llandeilo. It is the subject of a Romantic poem by John Dyer (1699-1757) and the hill was the site of an Iron Age fort. For Piper, the cumulative collage technique perhaps represented the layers of history associated with the site.

Piper produced collages throughout the late 1930s, using a technique derived from Cubist *papier collé*. He saw an exhibition of Pablo Picasso's *papier collés* in Paris in 1935 that left him 'deeply impressed by the intense poetry that he

[Picasso] generated by putting two or three bits of Ingrés paper on a white sheet, with a few ink marks here and there'. Piper's collages were often made on the spot. The materials used here include scraps salvaged from the floors of the Curwen Press, for whom Piper produced lithographs. The church and barn in the foreground are made from a print by Edward Bawden (1903-1989).

From childhood, Piper was passionately interested in art and architecture. Initially compelled to work in his father's solicitors firm, with his mother's support he eventually studied art. His work turned to abstraction after visiting Paris in 1933. In 1937 he married the writer Myfanwy Evans (1911-1997) and together they worked on the influential magazine *AXIS*. He was later commissioned as a war artist and painted numerous major buildings in case of their destruction by bombing. *CT*

118. Ceri Richards
(b. Dunvant, Glamorgan 1903;
d. London 1971)

Cycle of Nature
1944

Oil on canvas, 102.2 x 152.7cm

Purchased with assistance of the
Knapping Fund, 1959

NMW A 219

This chaotic mass is a combination of animal, human and vegetable forms. It is possible to discern legs, arms, feet, leaves, grapes, vines, bulbous forms and veins, which connect back to the earth and are full of what appears to be blood. The imagery is based on Dylan Thomas's poem *The force that through the green fuse drives the flower* (1933). The second stanza reads:

The force that drives the water through the rocks
Drives my red blood; that dries the mouthing streams
Turns mine to wax.
And I am dumb to mouth unto my veins
How at the mountain spring the same mouth sucks.

The rocks, blood, veins and water imagery is evident in the painting. The poem itself describes the natural cycle of death, rebirth and regeneration, but also Thomas's fear of growing old and dying.

Cycle of Nature was painted in Cardiff and exhibited in 1946 at the Redfern Gallery under the title *The Green Projector*.

Richards was born in Dunvant, a small mining village near Swansea. He studied at Swansea School of Art and the Royal College of Art in London. He first developed an interest in Dylan Thomas's poems in 1944. In 1945 he was commissioned to illustrate Thomas's poem for *Poetry London*, for which Richards produced three lithographs. *Cycle of Nature* is his second major painting to be inspired by this poem.

After Dylan Thomas's death in 1953, Richards was asked to design a drop-cloth and décor for the memorial service. This led him into a long period of producing homages to Dylan Thomas. *MM*

Art after 1950

Right: detail from *The Actor* by David Hockney (No. 126)

National Museum Cardiff is Wales's principal museum of modern and contemporary art. We seek to present the best of recent and contemporary practice in Wales in painting, sculpture, print-making, photography, silver, ceramics and new media against a British and international context. The Museum received additional government funding from 1972 specifically in order to build up the holdings of twentieth century art, and in 1989 received over six hundred works by Graham Sutherland from the artist's foundation. Since 1993 the Museum has worked closely with the Derek Williams Trust. The Trust both adds to the mid-twentieth century collection formed by Derek Williams (on extended loan to the Museum) and supports many of the Museum's acquisitions of modern art. Although largely unseen before the opening of new galleries in 2011, the Museum now has one of the best and most comprehensive collections of contemporary art in Britain.

In 2002 much of the art collection formed by the Welsh Arts Council between the 1950s and the 1970s also came to the Museum. Together with earlier acquisitions, this documents the transformation of the Welsh art world during the 1950s with the growth in art education and the arrival of Abstraction as an international language. Nevertheless the landscape has remained a central inspiration to many. More recently Welsh artists have often sought to develop a distinctive voice in a globalised, post-colonial world, exploring issues of national and cultural identity and environmental concerns.

Consequently the post-1950 collection ranges from the entirely abstract to the work of artists such as Bacon and Freud who share a preoccupation with the human figure. It is also strong in works that reference the pop culture of the 1960s and 1970s. More recently, it was expanded into the fields of conceptual art and of photography. Works in film and video by Welsh artists have complemented others acquired through the international Artes Mundi prize. Wales has also developed a vibrant craft scene since the 1980s, and is home to a number of makers with a substantial international reputation. Again with the support of the Derek Williams Trust, and others, we have developed an exceptional collection of contemporary ceramics, and have begun to add contemporary work to other areas of the applied art collections, especially silver and glass.

119. Martin Bloch
(b. Neisse, Silesia 1883;
d. London 1954)

Down from Bethesda Quarry
1951
Oil on canvas, 122.4 x 182.7cm
Given by the Contemporary
Art Society, 1956
NMW A 2256

The picture shows slate workers returning home from Penrhyn Quarry. Captured in the evening light, they cross the Pont y Twr bridge across the River Ogwen that connects the quarry to the town of Bethesda, Gwynedd. The landscape is as much the focus of the painting as the quarrymen. Emerging from the surrounding landscape, they are represented with dignity, with Bloch avoiding the temptation to romanticise their lives. His fluid brushwork and use of expressive colour points to his close associations with German Expressionism.

Bloch was born in Neisse, Silesia (now Nysa, Poland) in 1883. He studied in Berlin and Munich and in 1912 worked in Paris. He spent most of the First World War in Spain, returning to Berlin in 1919. His Jewish origins forced him to flee Germany in 1933 and he settled in London. Bloch first visited Wales in 1947, staying with friends in Bangor.

He visited again in 1950 and on each occasion returned to London via south Wales in order to visit fellow émigré artist Josef Herman in Ystradgynlais. Bloch's paintings contribute to an interesting history of émigré artists in Wales. Herman and Heinz Koppel also drew inspiration from working-class life in Wales to produce socially engaged paintings rooted in European expressionism.

The painting was commissioned by the Arts Council for the major exhibition *Sixty Paintings for '51*, part of the Festival of Britain. This called for participating artists to 'paint a large work, not less than 45 by 60 inches on a subject of their own choice.' Bloch's choice of a Welsh subject for such an important commission underlines the importance of the quarry landscapes of north Wales in his later years. *NT*

120. Josef Herman
(b. Warsaw, Poland 1911;
d. London 2000)

Miners Singing
1951
Oil on board, plaster ground,
43.5 x 121.6cm
Purchased, 1992
NMW A 1674

Choirs had begun in the mining communities in the late nineteenth century and became an important social activity. Herman has used the subject to address the broader concerns of working life in the mines, showing that camaraderie and solidarity were important aspects. In this image it appears the men are taking a break, as they have put down their tools but still have their lamps on their heads. There is no distinction between the faces; they are all alike, adding to the sense of solidarity.

Miners Singing is a study for a larger work called *Miners*, produced for the 'Minerals of the Island' Pavilion at the 1951 Festival of Britain. The exhibition was intended to mark the centenary of the Great Exhibition of 1851 and showcase British arts, architecture, science, technology and industrial design.

Herman was born in Poland to Jewish parents. He attended Warsaw School of Art in 1930-32. He fled his homeland in 1938 to avoid anti-Semitic persecution. He went first to Belgium and then through France to Britain, where in 1940 he initially settled in Glasgow. From 1943 to 1944 he spent a brief time in London before moving to the south Wales mining village of Ystradgynlais. Here he lived among the mining community, drawing them while they worked. He intended to stay a fortnight, but lived there for the next eleven years. The miners affectionately nicknamed him *Joe-bach* (little Joe), and he was honorary chairman of the local male voice choir. Herman became famous in the 1950s for his portrayal of Welsh miners, a subject which he often returned to even after he left Wales. *MM*

121. Sir Terry Frost
(b. Leamington Spa, Warwickshire 1915;
d. Hayle, Cornwall 2003)

Brown Harbour
1952
Oil on canvas, 88.7 x 117cm
Bequeathed by Margaret Davies, 1963
NMW A 2167

This picture is from a group that established Terry Frost's early reputation. It is one of the last paintings acquired by Margaret Davies, and demonstrates how she remained aware of the latest work by emerging young artists.

Growing up in the Midlands, Frost had a variety of jobs in small local workshops and in a factory. He was called up in 1939, and was captured in the battle for Crete in 1941. He was held in Stalag 383 in Germany, where he spent time drawing and painting, and became a close friend of the artist Adrian Heath (1920-1992). Frost resolved to attend art college and pursue an artistic career when the War ended.

After the War Frost lived briefly in St Ives, before studying at Camberwell School of Art with Victor Pasmore (1908-1998). Pasmore and Heath were beginning to test ways in which observing the world through still-life and portraiture corresponded with a formal language of painting and collage, where colour and form possessed their own effect.

Frost returned to St Ives in 1950, to be near friends like Peter Lanyon (1918-1964) and Bryan Wynter (1915-1975), who understood the importance of intense personal experience of the landscape.

As Frost's work became distinctively his own, from 1949 to 1953, these twin influences fused. His paintings were organized with crisp lines, rectangles and circles painted or pasted on as collage, and contrasts of colour emphasising the construction of space. Their subjects were views and journeys along coasts, with the most characteristic evoking a very specific experience: his walk along the quay in St Ives harbour near his tiny terraced cottage. *MT*

122. Dame Barbara Hepworth
(b. Wakefield, Yorkshire 1903;
d. St Ives, Cornwall 1975)

Oval sculpture (Delos)
1955
Painted wood, 85.8 x 119.3 x 75cm
Purchased, 1982
NMW A 2416

This is one of a series of large wooden sculptures carved by Barbara Hepworth between 1954 and 1956. The series was made from giant logs of 'scented' guarea – a tropical hardwood shipped to her studio in St Ives from Nigeria. She later recalled the material as 'the most beautiful, hard, lovely warm timber… I was never happier.'

Hepworth began the series following an extended trip to Greece where she immersed herself in the country's landscape, myths and antiquities, writing 'In Greece the inspiration was fantastic. I ran up the hills like a hare with my notebook, to get there first and have the impact of solitude. I made many drawings for new sculptures called 'Delphi', 'Delos', 'Mycenae,' 'Epidauros' and 'Santorin'. These forms were my experience there.'

Although not a literal transcription of place, some commentators have related the two tunnel-like holes that pierce the sculpture to the caves found on the Greek island of Delos. This penetration of the sculptural block was one of Hepworth's most important innovations. She first developed this idea in 1931 and it became a key motif in her work. By piercing the block, she opened up space around and through the sculpture. Here the play between interior and exterior is accentuated by the white painted internal surface contrasting with the smooth forms of the polished outer surface.

Oval sculpture (Delos) and the other large-scale guarea sculptures are some of the most ambitious and important carvings in the history of British sculpture. Few British sculptors have attempted to work in wood on this scale and they remain an important testament to Hepworth's continued commitment to carving in the post-war period. *NT*

123. Peter Lanyon
(b. St Ives, Cornwall 1918;
d. St Ives 1964)

Beach Girl
1961
Oil on canvas, 107 x 153cm
Purchased with the assistance of the Art
Fund and the Derek Williams Trust, 2006
NMW A 27155

Peter Lanyon is one of many artists associated with St Ives in Cornwall, where his family were from and where he grew up. He knew the artists who moved to Cornwall, such as Adrian Stokes, Ben Nicholson, Barbara Hepworth and Naum Gabo, and his contemporaries included Sir Terry Frost, Patrick Heron and Brian Wynter. In the 1950s and 1960s they became known for vivid near-abstract painting, which often took the experience of landscape as a starting point, and deployed effects of colour, texture and the illusions of flatness and space on the surface of paintings.

Beach Girl points to a number of ways in which Lanyon's work is distinct within this group of artists. He felt he had a distinct connectedness to the local landscape. Earlier in his career, for example, he described Cornish mining landscapes through dense images that suggested dark hollowed out spaces and jagged forms. He depicted harbours and shores around estuaries as places of tidal flow. In both respects he saw the human body as a metaphor of landscape and seascape, and vice versa.

We might, therefore, imagine the title of this painting as a juxtaposition – beach and girl as a double image – as well as trying to understand it as based on, perhaps, a drawing of a girl on a beach. The dynamism of the swirling breaking wave-like form creates an active sweep, set against a sensuous soft stillness. As Lanyon commented, 'I paint the weather and high places and places where solids and fluids meet. The Junction of sea and cliff, wind and cliff, the human body and places all contribute'. *MT*

124. Francis Bacon
(b. Dublin, Ireland 1909;
d. Madrid, Spain 1992)

Study for Self-Portrait
1963
Oil on canvas, 165.2 x 142.6cm
Purchased, 1978
NMW A 218

This appears at first sight to be a casual portrait, as though Bacon has put aside his newspaper and cigarettes to pose for a photograph, or in this case a painting. Although it is called study, it is a finished work.

Despite the casualness of the pose this painting exhibits the classic hallmarks of a Francis Bacon portrait, which are distorted and fragmented facial features, disjointed limbs and a figure set within a flat, simple domestic interior. The most significant element of Bacon's portraits is the distortion of the facial features. The paint is smeared across the main features of the face, almost entirely obliterating the mouth, nose and eyes. The artist once said that he did not paint a person's soul or psyche, but their appearance as it is affected by their behaviour.

Bacon was particularly fixated on the issue of mortality. The body as he depicts it often resembles raw flesh on the cusp of putrefaction. His interest in the raw meat paintings of Chaïm Soutine (1893-1943) and documentary photographs of slaughterhouses filtered into his work.

Bacon was born in Dublin to English parents. As his homosexuality caused friction with his family, he left Ireland aged sixteen and drifted for a number of years in London, Berlin and Paris. After seeing drawings by Picasso in Paris, he decided to become an artist. Despite never receiving formal academic training, Bacon became the most renowned British portrait painter of the post-war era. *MM*

125. Richard Smith
(b. Letchworth 1931)

Staggerly
1963
Oil on canvas, 153 x 244cm
Purchased, 1977
NMW A 2235

Staggerly is made from three separate canvases hung together to create an irregular-shaped painting. Although seemingly abstract, the painting is inspired by packets of Lucky Strike cigarettes. Picking up on the brand's distinctive design – a red circle on the white background – three packets are shown 'staggered' against a background of red and blue banding. *Staggerly* has been painted in both flat colour and more expressive brushwork.

In the 1950s Smith was influenced by the latest developments in the United States, in particular the painting of the American Abstract Expressionists. He began to produce large, abstract canvases painted in fluid, gestural brushwork. Living and working in New York between 1959 and 1961 he began to be aware of the power of consumer culture. This led to paintings that combined the high art of abstraction with the popular culture of advertising and commercial packaging. As Smith explained in 1966, 'The carton is an incessant theme in present-day civilisation: shops are full of boxes and you see these before you see the goods; they practically stand in for the goods – it is not just a question of labelling or depiction. Everything comes in boxes: you buy boxes when you are shopping, you do not buy visible goods; you don't buy cigarettes, only cartons.'

In 1962 Smith made a film called *Trailer* which focused on packets of cigarettes viewed from different angles. This film influenced the paintings of the following year including *Staggerly*. The scale of the Lucky Strike designs in this painting suggests the influence of advertising hoardings. *Staggerly* is an important example of Smith's key innovation of combining Pop and abstraction in ambitious, bold paintings. *NT*

126. David Hockney
(b. Bradford 1937)

The Actor
1964

Acrylic on canvas, 166.5 x 167.3cm

Purchased with the assistance of the Derek Williams Trust, the Art Fund and the Honourable James Butler Charitable Trust, 1999

NMW A 13523

The room depicted in this painting could either be an actual living room or a stage setting with theatre curtains on either side. The brightly patterned sofa and palm tree patterned cushion both show the interior decoration style of the 1960s. The figure appears stalky and stone-like. It is possibly based on a statue of the ancient Egyptian Pharaoh Akhenaten IV (1390-1352BC). It may also signify the artistic revolution in the reign of Akhenaten. Hockney visited Egypt in 1963 for the *Sunday Times* and there is a range of Egyptian literary and historic references in Hockney's work during this period. Similar heads appear in *Hockney's Four Heads (Egyptian)*, 1963 and *California Art Collector*, 1964.

Hockney trained at the School of Art in Bradford and the Royal College of Art. *The Actor* was painted within a six-week period when Hockney was teaching at the University of Iowa in the summer of 1964. He found the landscape of Iowa City uninspiring, besides the great thunderstorms. As a result four of the five paintings he produced there had nothing to do with Iowa, but continued with themes he had begun exploring in California.

Hockney became a leading British Pop artist, achieving international status in the 1960s. *The Actor* is the only Hockney painting in the Museum's collection, and as such it makes a major contribution to the significant group of British paintings of the 1960s by figures such as Francis Bacon and Patrick Caulfield. *MM*

127. Sir Peter Blake
(b. Dartford, Kent 1932)

Kamikaze
1965
Cryla and collage on board,
78.7 x 48.2cm
Purchased with the assistance of the Art
Fund and the Derek Williams Trust, 2006
NMW A 28054

Kamikaze is an imaginary Japanese-American wrestler. The name Kamikaze is taken from the Japanese pilots of light bomber aircraft trained to crash their planes in suicide missions against allied ships in the Pacific War. This is supported by various collage elements including a toy Japanese 'Zero' plane glued to the support, a collage of photographs of Kamikaze pilots taken from magazines, together with a Kamikaze armband and a traditional Japanese wrestler mask sitting above the work, wearing a knitted mask made to match the painting. It exemplifies elements of popular culture of the 1960s including the use of comic strip style lettering. *Kamikaze* was included in Robert Frazer's seminal one-man exhibition of Blake's work from 1965.

Blake has always produced works in series and the wrestling figures is his most protracted and diverse series. This work was created in the same year as another wrestler work called *The Masked Zebra Kid* (Tate).

Blake emerged in the early 1960s as a key member of the Pop Art movement. He studied art at Gravesend Technical College and School of Art from 1946 to 1951. Blake went on to study painting at the Royal College of Art in London where his tutor was 'proto-pop artist' Ruskin Spear. It was at this time that he began to draw inspiration from popular and commercial culture. He has worked in a range of media such as painting, collage, sculpture, engraving and printmaking. In addition he has produced commercial graphic art, most famously the cover of The Beatles' *Sgt Pepper's Lonely Hearts Club Band* album released in 1967. *MM*

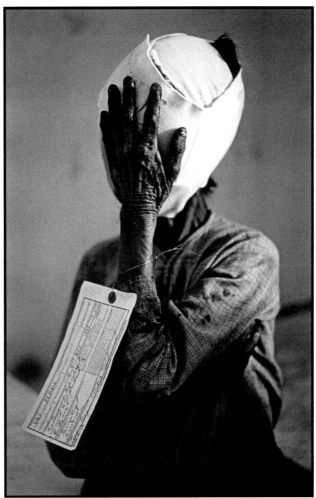

128. Philip Jones Griffiths
(b. Rhuddlan, Denbighshire 1936; d. London 2008)

Civilian victim, Vietnam 1967
Photograph (silver gelatin print), 51 x 41cm
Purchased, 1996
NMW A 12750

A burn victim holds up a blackened hand to her head, mummified with bandages, tagged as though an exhibit, in a gesture of blind suffering. The simplicity of the composition, light falling from the right, seems to intensify the feeling of mute and defenceless suffering. The tag on the woman's wrist bears the initials VNC, indicating a Vietnamese civilian. Jones Griffiths wrote 'This was unusual. Wounded civilians were normally tagged VCS (Vietcong suspect) and all dead peasants were posthumously elevated to the rank of VCC (Vietcong confirmed)'.

Jones Griffiths arrived in Vietnam in 1966, already a veteran photojournalist. He travelled the country for four years, documenting the suffering of the ordinary Vietnamese. As a Welsh republican, he felt an affinity with the Vietnamese, seeing a parallel between the American presence in Vietnam and Wales's subjugation by England. His graphic, unflinching images remained largely unpublished until 1971, when he published *Vietnam Inc*. This iconic book proved instrumental in turning American public opinion against the war. *Time* magazine called it 'the best book of photo-reportage of war ever published' and the legendary French photographer Henri Cartier-Bresson (1908-2004) later wrote 'Not since Goya has anyone portrayed war like Philip Jones Griffiths'.

Jones Griffiths trained as a pharmacist and worked in London, while photographing part-time for the *Manchester Guardian*. In 1963 he began to work full time as a photojournalist, covering the war in Algeria. He became an associate of the prestigious Magnum photographic agency in 1967 and in the 1980s served for an unprecedented five years as the agency's President. He is now recognized as one of the most fearless, radical and humane photographers of the twentieth century. *CT*

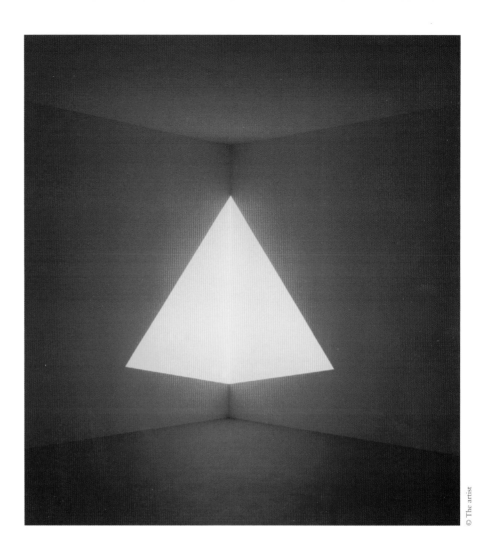

129. James Turrell
(b. Pasadena, California, USA 1943)

Raethro Pink
1968
Light projection, dimensions vary with installation
Purchased with the assistance of the Art Fund, the Derek Williams Trust and the Bilstone Foundation, 2008
NMW A 29355

James Turrell creates installations using light and space. His practice is rooted in the expansive visual quality and intense light of the Southern Californian landscape. Born in 1943, he studied psychology, mathematics and art history before completing a Fine Art degree in 1966. In that year he rented the former Mendota Hotel in Ocean Park, California, turning it into a studio and exhibition space. Sealing the building from the sound and light outside, he experimented with projected light. Over the next three years he produced his seminal series of projection works, which include *Raethro Pink*. These were formed by light projected across the corner of a white room from a modified quartz halogen projector. Making light a tangible material, they appear to be geometrical shapes suspended in space. *Raethro Pink* is a rhomboid of pink light which gives the impression of a luminous three-dimensional pyramid hovering in the darkness. This effect is enhanced on moving around the space, but the form disappears into a flat plane as one approaches the corner of the room.

Turrell's work is a form of minimalist abstraction. His projection pieces are physically simple but psychologically haunting and conceptually complex. Through optical effects alone, they acquire an almost bodily presence. They seem to construct perceptual windows through a solid surface, a quality Turrell went on to explore in his later sky space installations – rooms from which one can view the sky from an opening in the roof. He has created several in Britain, including at the Yorkshire Sculpture Park and in Kielder Forest, Northumberland. *OF*

130. David Nash
(b. Esher, Surrey 1945)

Table with Cubes
1971-2
Wood, height 98.1cm; width 155cm;
depth 112cm
Given by the Contemporary Art Society
for Wales, 1980
NMW 2423

This work comes from early in Nash's artistic career. He had been living and working in a disused chapel in Blaenau Ffestiniog, in north Wales for three years, where he is still based. The work demonstrates the fundamental interests that have sustained his practice for the subsequent decades.

Like some of his contemporaries, Nash was searching for simplicity both in his life and his art. He was of a generation who saw that 'work' and 'way of life' had to be in harmony and express consistent values.

In 1971 he began working in an area of wooded hillside down the valley from the town's industrial surroundings. He later commented that he began to identify with the idea of 'tree' not of 'wood' as being his material. He wanted to express how cutting down or planting trees was an expression of how people related to the land.

Table with Cubes is exactly that: a table with six cubes arranged loosely on it. A table suggests a function, yet all it appears to be for is to have some shapes arranged on it. It is also hard to see it as abstract or even symbolic. Instead, as it becomes more familiar, it brings associations into the space of a museum. Its roughness speaks of the outdoors, while the idea of arrangement on a table evokes ceremony. It is a little mysterious even while feeling immediate and rough, just like the woodland which gave up its material.

Today David Nash is regarded as one of the leading artists of his generation. His work is particularly well known in Japan, the United States and continental Europe. *MT*

131. Graham Sutherland
(b. London 1903; d. London 1980)

Trees with G-Shaped Form I
1972
Oil on canvas, 117 x 172cm
Purchased, 1973
NMW A 220

Two broad tree trunks frame a G-shaped knot of roots, twigs and vegetation that emerges from the lush, dank gloom. The location is the beach of an estuary and water has washed the roots smooth and bare and their paleness contrasts with the damp green banks behind. The central form suggests tension and balance, poised as it is between the solid, immobile moss-covered trunks from which bulbous growths protrude.

Graham Sutherland was foremost a nature painter. He was fascinated by the exuberance he perceived in the contrast of darkness and light, decay and life. He wrote of the attraction of the 'exultant strangeness' of places he was inspired by and explained it was the 'element of disquiet' he discovered in them that drew him. This work is based on a tree root he came across near Benton Castle in Pembrokeshire and which he painted

a number of times. He first visited Pembrokeshire in 1934 and was profoundly influenced by the landscape he encountered there. When he returned in the last decade of his life he found himself inspired once more and sorely regretted his time away. He embarked afresh on a series of paintings, including this one, which drew on the 'curiously charged atmosphere' he discovered in the Welsh landscape.

Sutherland first achieved wide recognition as a leading figure in the neo-Romantic movement and went on to become the pre-eminent painter of his generation, winning both critical and popular acclaim. While this work was purchased soon after it was painted, the Museum's collection also includes a diverse group of several hundred works spanning Sutherland's more than fifty-year career, which he gave to Wales. *RF*

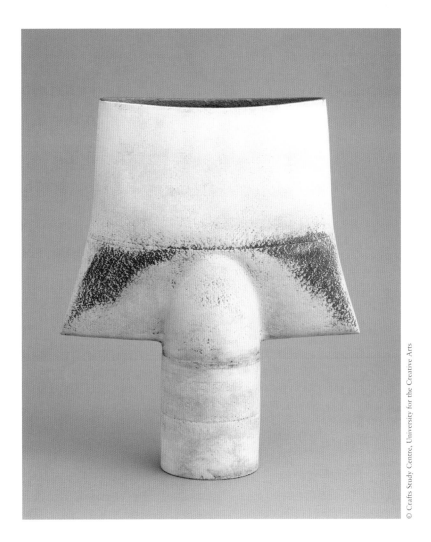

132. Hans Coper

(b. Chemnitz, Germany 1920;
d. Frome, Somerset 1981)

Vase
1973
Stoneware, height 38.2cm
Purchased, 1974
NMW A 32082

Coper has been described as 'quite simply … the most important post-war potter in the UK, if not world-wide. His importance stems both from the formidable body of work, which shows how wheel-thrown clay can be the vehicle for sculptural expression of the highest order, and from his effect as a teacher' (Oliver Watson, *British Studio Pottery: The Victoria and Albert Museum Collection*, 1990).

Form was of primary concern to Coper. This abstract, spade-shaped vase, assembled from different wheel-thrown parts, has considerable strength of presence. He began to create spade forms in 1966 and they were first shown in public a year later, at a joint exhibition with Lucie Rie (1902-1995) in Rotterdam.

In addition to form, the interplay between light and dark surface colour is an essential aspect of his work. This vase has been painted with a dark slip, over which a white slip has been applied to retain areas of dark colour. It has a characteristic matt, textured surface, which has a tactile yet austere quality.

Coper left Germany for England in 1939. Following a brief period of internment and service in the Pioneer Corps, he began working in 1946 as assistant to Lucie Rie at the Albion Mews Pottery. They worked together until 1958, when Coper left to set up his own studio, eventually settling near Frome, Somerset, in 1967. Rie and Coper had a deep and lasting influence on each other and their work is often discussed in conjunction.

There are twenty-eight pieces by Coper in the Museum's collection, dating between the late 1940s and 1973. *RC*

133. Keith Arnatt

(b. Oxford 1930;
d. Tintern, Monmouthshire 2008)

The Visitors
1974-6

46 silver gelatin prints,
each 50.6 x 40.6cm

Purchased with the assistance of the
Derek Williams Trust, 2010

NMW A 29605-29650

In *The Visitors* Keith Arnatt photographs day-trippers at the popular tourist destination of Tintern Abbey. Arnatt's photographs tell us little about the ruined Cistercian abbey, instead focusing on the visitors themselves, and giving glimpses into their backgrounds and personalities. This is one of his earliest photographic projects. It followed a previous focus on performance and conceptual work, which had already established his reputation internationally.

In 1969 Arnatt moved to Tintern, Monmouthshire, and began to teach fine art at Newport College of Art. His interest in photography developed from his background as a conceptual artist and was encouraged by David Hurn who established the photography department at Newport in 1973. Through Hurn, Arnatt was introduced to the work of other photographers such as August Sander and Diane Arbus, both of whose influence is clearly discernable in the tightly framed, double-portraits of *The Visitors*.

Although *The Visitors* may appear to be conventional portraits or holiday snapshots, they retain the intellectual rigour of his earlier conceptual work. Because there is a distance between Arnatt and his sitters, the series operates as a witty investigation into our responses to being photographed. Arnatt explained, 'Getting someone to pose for a snapshot will usually elicit a response which is quite typical and yet different from the formal studio portrait. It is the range and nuances of such responses which is the subject of my Visitor photographs.'

The Museum acquired forty-six prints from *The Visitors* series. They join two other important photographic series by Arnatt – *Miss Grace's Lane* (1986-7) and *Howler's Hill* (1987-8). *NT*

134. Sir Kyffin Williams
(b. Llangefni, Anglesey 1918;
d. Llanfair Pwllgwyngyll, Anglesey 2006)

Farmers on the Carneddau
About 1980
Oil on canvas, 121.7 x 183cm
Purchased, 1993
NMW A 2364

Kyffin Williams painted the landscape of north Wales for sixty years, and this picture contains much that is familiar in his work – the mountains under heavy clouds and a sombre sky, and in the foreground hill farmers with their flat caps and sticks accompanied by their sheepdogs. The predominant colours are olive-green, slate-grey, ochre and umber, and the paint is applied with a palette knife in thick, bold swathes of pigment. He also painted the sea, and was a fine and idiosyncratic portraitist, but his monumental landscapes of Snowdonia became hugely popular icons of Wales. Here the subject is the Carneddau ('the cairns') range in northern Snowdonia.

Even when Williams worked in London as an art master at Highgate School (1944-1973) he returned in his imagination to the landscape in which he had been brought up, and which he had

come to know as a trainee land agent before the Second World War. He only became a painter after being invalided out of the army in 1941, and developed a strongly personal style characterised by his bold application of paint, sombre tonality and considerable degree of abstraction, which recalls early twentieth-century Expressionism.

Williams held his first one-man exhibition at Colnaghi's in 1948 and his inclusion in the Arts Council of Great Britain's *Twenty-five Paintings by Contemporary Welsh Artists* in the year following confirmed his standing as a major presence in Wales. His work was bought by many private collectors, including Margaret Davies, and by Welsh institutions. Later in life he was loved as a wonderful teller of stories, and during this period he made a major contribution to many artistic causes in Wales. *OF*

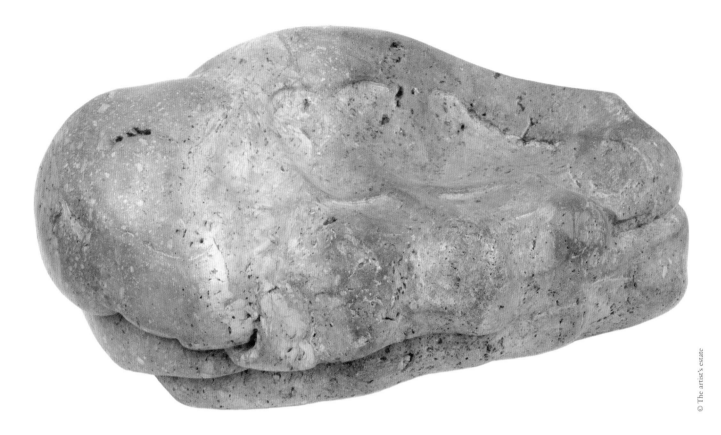

135. Barry Flanagan
(b. Prestatyn, Denbighshire 1941;
d. Ibiza, Spain 2009)

Carving No. 5
1982
Marble, 26 x 73 x 51cm
Purchased with the assistance of the
Derek Williams Trust, 2009
NMW A 29405

Carving No. 5 belongs to a series of
stone carvings made by Barry Flanagan in
the early 1980s. He worked closely with
skilled stone carvers in Pietrasanta, Italy.
Squeezing lumps of clay in his hand he
created models that were then passed
to the carvers who enlarged and copied
them in marble. The level of detail in the
final carving includes traces of the artist's
finger prints transcribed from the original
clay.

By carving marble to look like modelled
clay, Flanagan makes a sculptural joke
that references one of the most enduring
debates in modern sculpture: the relative
merits between carving and modelling.
Carving No. 5 is a witty riposte to the
modernist doctrine of 'truth to materials'
that dominated sculpture for much of the

first half of the twentieth century (see no.
106). This questioning of received truth
is a consistent theme in Flanagan's work,
tying together a diverse body of work
produced since the 1960s.

Flanagan studied at Birmingham College
of Art & Crafts and St Martin's School
of Art, London. In the 1960s abstract
sculpture made from industrial materials
such as plastic and steel dominated the
teaching at St Martin's. Flanagan began
to disrupt this orthodoxy by making
sculptures from more ephemeral
materials such as sand, cloth, twigs and
even light. Along with other younger
artists who emerged from St Martin's in
the 1960s he tested the boundaries and
definitions of what sculpture should and
could be. *NT*

136. Bridget Riley
(b. London 1931)

Kashan
1984
Oil on linen, 211.5 x 171cm
Purchased with the assistance of the
Derek Williams Trust, 1999
NMW A 14059

Kashan forms part of Riley's series of vibrant stripe canvases dating from the period between 1980 and 1985 known as the Egyptian paintings. Riley had been experimenting with colour since the late 1960s – a shift from the black and white works that made her reputation, but her palette was transformed by a visit in 1979 to Egypt. There, the light-saturated clarity of the North African landscape suggested new possibilities for unlocking visual sensation through a combination of simplified form and intensified colour.

Kashan is made up of the irregular play of stripes across a canvas, arranged intuitively rather than by structure. Each colour band is sharply distinct, but, like the experience of viewing colours in nature, cannot be perceived in isolation. The visual effect of this interaction is the emergence of a perceptual plane – 'the horizontal spread of coloured light' – as the colours shift and dazzle, the surface buzzes and pulses, shimmers and hums. It exists through the act of looking, conjured by the viewer, to be transformed again in the blink of an eye.

Riley has a keen appreciation of the historical traditions of painting and the art of the past. For her, the point of departure is always colour and shape rather than subject, and each painting remains untitled until it has been finished, viewed and experienced. Riley says of this process 'I try to title my paintings according to their spirit ... I usually draw on memory, memories of sensations in the past'. *Kashan* refers to the Iranian province of the same name, a traditional centre of the silk trade. *BD*

137. Terry Setch
(b. Lewisham, London 1936)

Night Watch
1985
Oil and encaustic wax on canvas,
168.7 x 306cm
Purchased, 1985
NMW A 2177

This is one of a number of major works by Terry Setch in the collection. These reflect his status as one of the best-known artists working in Wales, where he has lived for more than four decades since arriving here, aged twenty-eight, in 1964.

In the 1980s what was termed by critics as a 'new spirit' in painting led to Setch's work becoming well known for its grand physical presence and innovative, powerful techniques. This physical and visual impact often fuses with the social and political dimensions of his work. For example, many of his best-known paintings describe a long artistic relationship with the beach near his home in Penarth, on the south Wales coast. In these he incorporated materials such as wax and plastics sealing in objects gathered from the location. As much as describing landscape, these works raise

our awareness of pollution, vandalism and the corruption of land and sea over time.

Night Watch is one of a series of his explicitly political paintings. Setch's wife Dianne was one of the earliest activists in the women's peace camp at RAF Greenham Common, in Berkshire. They were resisting the use of the base for American nuclear cruise missiles. Setch visited the camp twice. His paintings evoke a damp, wooded setting where plastic sheets were stretched to create shelter. The forms of monumental figures seem to emerge out of an organic mass. The title refers to Rembrandt's famous painting, turning immortalisation of a group of civic guardians into a tribute to the watch kept by the women of the camp. *MT*

138. Lucian Freud
(b. Berlin 1922)

The Painter's Brother, Stephen
1985-6
Oil on canvas, 51.0 x 40.9cm
Purchased, 1986
NMW A 223

Lucian Freud rarely works from professional models, preferring instead to use friends and family as sitters. This painting focuses on the head and shoulders of his elder brother, who dispassionately returns our gaze. It demonstrates the way Freud's unflinching examination on the physical appearance of his sitters charges his work with a psychological intensity. A year after this painting was completed the art critic Robert Hughes described Freud as 'the greatest living realist painter'.

Freud, whose grandfather was the founder of psychoanalysis Sigmund Freud, was born in Berlin in 1922. He moved to Britain with his family in 1933. In 1939, after a brief period at Central School of Arts and Crafts, Freud enrolled at Cedric Morris's East Anglia School of Painting and Drawing. Morris's teaching and the idiosyncratic ethos of the School seemed to have appealed to Freud during these formative years. In 1981 he wrote 'Cedric taught me to paint and more important to keep at it. He did not say much but let me watch him at work. I have always admired his paintings and everything about him.'

In 1940 Freud painted a small portrait of Morris, which was acquired in 1998 for the Museum's collection. Morris was certainly an early and important influence on Freud. Comparison of *The Painter's Brother, Stephen* with a portrait by Morris such as *The Sisters* (no. 115) reveal a shared intensity of observation and psychological penetration. This gives their portraits an existential power that suggests much about the often complex relationship between artist and sitter. *NT*

139. Peter Prendergast

(b. Abertridwr, Glamorgan 1946;
d. Deiniolen, Gwynedd 2007)

Blaenau Ffestiniog
1993
Oil on canvas, 122.3 x 305.2cm
Purchased, 1993
NMW A 2533

This landscape depicts the slate quarry of Blaenau Ffestiniog in north Wales, just south of Bangor where Peter Prendergast lived at the time. Amgueddfa Cymru commissioned the painting to hang in the restaurant at National Museum Cardiff. The large scale, bright colours, thickly applied paint and heavy outlining in black are all strong characteristics of Prendergast's landscape paintings. The expressiveness of the brushstrokes and the thickness of the paint imply the cragginess and climatic changeability of the north-Wales landscape. The artist saw beauty in the hewn industrialised landscape of Wales, having grown up in a Welsh mining village.

Prendergast always began a composition with numerous drawings before beginning to paint in order to understand the landscape he was representing, often adding new sections of paper to extend the image to a wider view.

Prendergast's father was a coal miner who had come over from Ireland. He was taught art at Cwm Aber school by Gomer Lewis, who had a profound effect on him. He went on to study professionally at Cardiff College of Art and the Slade School of Art in London where he was taught by Frank Auerbach from 1964 to 1967. Prendergast felt there was a spirituality about the Welsh landscape, which he aimed to capture. In an interview with Robert Armstrong, Prendergast said: 'My father was digging out coal to make profits for other people. But then coal keeps people's houses warm. Painting keeps people's souls warm.' *MM*

140. Frank Auerbach
(b. Berlin 1931)

Park Village East – Winter
1998-9
Oil on canvas, 102.5 x 152.5cm
Purchased with the assistance of the
Derek Williams Trust and
the Art Fund, 2000
NMW A 17483

Park Village East is a street near Regent's Park, close to the artist's studio in London. With the exception of the human figure, the inner suburbs of north London have provided Frank Auerbach with perhaps his most important and enduring subject. Between 1994 and 1999 Auerbach produced a series paintings of Park Village East, capturing the street at different times of the year.

Auerbach begins a landscape by making numerous sketches in the chosen location. Six pencil and ink sketches for *Park Village East – Winter* were retained by the artist and were also acquired by the Museum. Auerbach uses the sketches as guides to paint the final work in the studio. A process of painting and scraping down is followed by an intense period of work to realise the final composition. A painting is finished when Auerbach achieves what he describes as a 'reinvention of the physical world'.

The energy and immediacy of the sketches for *Park Village East – Winter* have been transferred to the final painting. The thick impasto – a characteristic of Auerbach's surfaces – gives the painting an almost sculptural presence.

Auerbach is one of the most important figurative painters working today. Together with Lucian Freud, Francis Bacon and Leon Kossoff he is often grouped under the label School of London. What unites this grouping has been a strong commitment to figurative painting set against a wider shift towards pop, abstraction and conceptual art. Indeed Auerbach's knowledge and commitment to the traditions of painting are central to his practice. In *Park Village East – Winter* he openly acknowledges the composition of John Constable's *The Hay Wain* (National Gallery, London). *NT*

141. Bethan Huws
(b. Bangor, Gwynedd 1961)

Boats
1983-2000
Glass and maple vitrine with ten rush boat models, 137 x 67 x 52.5cm (vitrine); 7 x 2 x 0.5cm (boats)
Purchased with the assistance of the Derek Williams Trust, 2000
NMW A 17597

Each one of these 'boats' is made from one stem of rush, which has been taken up from the root and shaped into the base of a boat bearing a mast. Some have flowers while others do not. Some are yellow and others green. There is individuality to each boat. There are fewer boats in this vitrine compared to some other works from this series. In this particular piece the boats are arranged according to the pattern of the wood grain. The grains represent rivers on which the boats sail, while others rest in pools represented by the knots in the wood.

The boats relate to a game played in north Wales where for generations children have made boats from reeds and raced them on the rivers and streams. As such there is a sense of longing back to childhood, but we are also aware that the boats have been stopped on their journey and held in space and time.

Huws trained at Middlesex Polytechnic and the Royal College of Art in London, before settling in Paris. Her work first received major public attention when she was selected for the *British Art Show 3* in 1990 alongside artists such as Mona Hatoum, Julian Opie and Gary Hume. Since then she has exhibited widely across Europe and the United States. *MM*

142. Donald Rodney
(b. Birmingham 1961; d. London 1998)

In the House of my Father
1996-7
Photograph on paper aluminium
(Chromogenic print), 122 x 153cm
Given by the Contemporary Art Society,
2000
NMW A 15878

Donald Rodney was one of a group of artists brought up in African-Caribbean communities in English provincial cities who, from their early twenties onwards, have created a vivid body of work. His closest associates included Sonia Boyce, Claudette Johnson, Ingrid Pollard, Keith Piper and Eddie Chambers. Their early work was united by an anger and directness which came from the situations they lived in. They adopted superficially simple techniques, underpinned by a sophisticated understanding of how images create impact and meanings. They often referred to mainstream media and popular culture, and addressed subjects like the Transatlantic slave trade as well as immediate political and social issues.

Rodney suffered from sickle-cell anaemia. This is a serious hereditary illness that particularly affects people of west African descent. He frequently endured periods of sickness and treatment. By 1986 he realised that he could use his illness as a means to express his experience as a young black British man. As his illness progressed, he made photographs and films, and designed objects from his hospital bed.

This image is one of his last. He first made a tiny house from flakes of his own skin held together with dressmaker's pins, then arranged a photograph of it in his own palm. The print when exhibited is large, so that the image looms towards us from the background of bedsheets.

The title reminds us that he owes his situation to his racial inheritance. On occasions since Rodney's death, the house itself has been exhibited alongside, with the title *My mother, My father, my sister, my brother*. MT

143. Tim Davies
(b. Haverfordwest, Pembrokeshire 1960)

Postcard Series II
2002
Card, 12 parts, each 27 x 22cm
Given by the Contemporary Art Society
for Wales, 2006
NMW A 28176

For this work Tim Davies cut out the figures from cards featuring women wearing Welsh 'national' dress. All we are left with is a ghostly trace of the women removed from their landscape settings. This work is part of a larger ongoing project in which the artist uses tourist postcards, many of which make reference to European national identities.

The dissemination of Welsh identity through national dress dates back to the nineteenth century. What is generally understood today as the Welsh 'national' dress - red cloaks and tall black hats - was largely a nineteenth-century invention derived from traditional clothes worn in rural communities. This style was promoted by Augusta Hall, Lady Llanover (1802-1896) who believed that the wearing of national dress, alongside

the use of the Welsh language, was key to protecting the country's national identity. At the same time prints and postcards of women wearing national costume became popular with an emerging tourist industry. Seen in this historical context, *Postcard Series II* can be seen as a comment on the way tourist images perpetuate narrow and perhaps unhelpful constructions of national identity.

Since becoming a prizewinner at the 1994 National Eisteddfod in Neath Davies has emerged as one of Wales's most important contemporary artists. Although his work often references the Welsh context, he has developed a practice in a wide range of media that is equally well placed to engage with other cultural contexts. In 2011 he represented Wales at the Venice Biennale. *NT*

144. James Rielly
(b. Wrexham, Denbighshire 1956)

Partially Buried
2004
Oil on canvas, 198.1 x 259.1cm
Given by the artist, 2006
NMW A 27903

Partially Buried makes reference to the Aberfan disaster of 1966 in which 144 people were killed (see no. 148). James Rielly, who was ten years old at the time of the disaster, has dealt with a subject of great tragedy in a simple and yet seemingly peaceful way. The background is painted in pale muted pastel colours as is the plain simple building, which is being engulfed by the black impenetrable mass. The simplicity conveys that of a child's drawing and also the silence described by survivors after the slag heap stopped moving. As a schoolchild in Wales, Rielly was deeply affected by the disaster and as with many of his contemporaries the memory is still with him. Rielly often uses childhood memories to form the basis of his paintings.

James Rielly trained at Gloucester College of Art and Design and Belfast College of Art. He now lives and works in France. His work focuses mainly on children and childhood memories, using photographs and stories from newspapers and magazines as a source of inspiration. Rielly's paintings often question or subvert idealized or sentimentalized views of childhood and draw out the sinister. Sometimes this may only be subtly implied and then perceived more strongly by the viewer. *MM*

145. Walter Keeler
(b. London 1942)

Selection of works
1994 and 2004

Stoneware, earthenware, length: 19.7cm
(stoneware teapot); 24.2cm (earthenware
teapot); 22.6cm (bowl)

Purchased, 1994 and 2004

NMW A 32277, 37260, 37263

Walter Keeler is one of the leading studio potters working in Britain. Having emerged from the vibrant studio pottery scene of the 1960s, his work is highly individual and energetic, yet remains functional. Keeler's early career was defined by his radical take on the medium of salt-glazed stoneware. Departing from convention, he threw each part of his objects separately and assembled them to create distinctive forms, often influenced by mundane items such as oil cans and milk churns. Keeler has used these techniques on a striking teapot, reminiscent of a watering can. The handle and upper body are mottled with a deep, orange-peel effect caused by the corrosive salt, which contrasts with the lightly dappled body.

The vibrant yellow teapot with green splashes and brown streaks represents Keeler's experimentation with colourfully glazed earthenware during the mid-1990s. This type of glaze is often described as Whieldon, as it was first developed by Thomas Whieldon in Staffordshire during the 1740s. The spiked handle and spout introduce an element of danger and play with the notion of functionality. The serving dish, made in 2004, illustrates Keeler's recent preference for using a subtle grey glaze, described by him as 'ink wash'. It emphasises the traces left behind by making processes, such as rhythmic striations on the surface of the dish caused by wheel-throwing.

Walter Keeler studied at Harrow School of Art from 1958 to 1963 where he was taught by Victor Margrie and Michael Casson. Since 1976 he has been based at Penallt, Monmouthshire. *RC*

Courtesy of the artist & Ceri Hand Gallery

146. Bedwyr Williams
(b. St Asaph, Denbighshire 1974)

Bard Attitude
2005
Photograph, 150 x 100cm
Purchased with the assistance of the
Derek Williams Trust, 2009
NMW A 29477

In *Bard Attitude* Bedwyr Williams photographs himself in the guise of the last Welsh bard as recounted in Thomas Gray's *The Bard* in 1757 (see no. 37). The photograph was made for the exhibition *Brought to Light* at Oriel Mostyn in 2006. Artists were invited to make or adapt work in response to works from the National Museum. Williams selected John Harrison's *The Bard* (1840), itself a copy after a painting by Phillipe Jacques de Loutherbourg of the hero of Gray's poem. In the photograph Williams copies the pose of Harrison's bard, undermining Gray's romantic vision by describing him as 'a cursing muppet, fiddling with a harp on a rock'.

Williams' work often makes reference to the culture of Wales, and in particular outside perceptions of this culture. Irreverent humour is often employed to question or undermine certain stereotypes. As a Welsh speaker growing up in the popular tourist areas of north Wales, Williams has described feeling like an outsider in his own country: 'The seaside towns of north Wales are strange places to be a Welsh speaker: Carls, Deans and Kyles mimic your every utterance in a mock Welsh accent. Leisure centre staff lampoon your name as you register for judo classes.'

After a period in London Williams returned to Wales in 2002 and is currently based in Caernarfon. Although perhaps best known as a performance artist, Williams works in a wide range of media including sculpture and installation. He is a leading figure in a younger generation of Welsh artists who choose to base themselves in Wales and produce work of international importance. *NT*

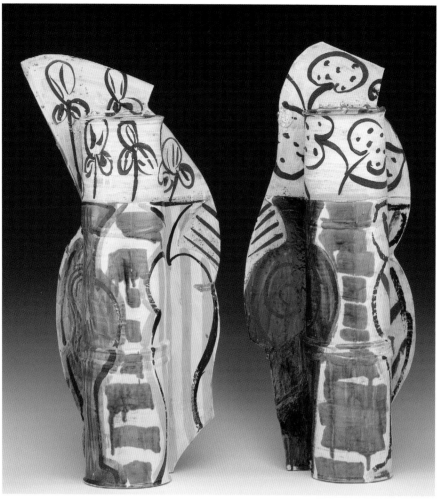

147. Betty Woodman
(b. Norwalk, Connecticut, USA 1930)

Diptych: The Balcony
2007

Glazed earthenware, epoxy resin, lacquer, paint, height: 92.2cm

Purchased with assistance from the Derek Williams Trust and the Art Fund, 2008

NMW A 39045

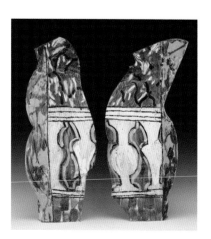

Looking at these two vessels from one side, we see a view from a Mediterranean balcony. In front of us a balustrade overlooks a background of vibrantly glossy colours that suggest flowers in a garden. As we look out we can visualise the balustrade and the garden continuing in the gap between the two vessels. Our imaginative participation in the work in a sense completes it.

On the other side, the two elements seem to represent a pair of colourful flower vases. All is not what it seems, though, for the artist uses the cylindrical vessels as a surface on which to depict other vessels. These painted vases run off the cylinder and onto the flat back section, interweaving two- and three-dimensional representation. It is as if the objects are both functional ceramics and paintings at the same time.

Strong marks of hand-throwing are especially evident on the flat backs, which have been cut from very large thrown forms. Woodman leaves us in no doubt that these are objects worked in clay, creating a tension between her painted visual illusions and the powerful physicality of the objects.

Diptych: The Balcony is a window onto the sunny world of Tuscany, where Woodman spends half her time. It typifies the qualities that have made her one of the most respected of American ceramic artists. Her free-spirited inventiveness, her bravado approach to colour, her sculptural sense of form and her delight in visual ambiguity are reminiscent of Picasso's ceramics. Her stature was confirmed in 2006 when she became the first living woman artist to be given a solo exhibition at the Metropolitan Museum, New York. *AR*

148. Shimon Attie
(b. Los Angeles, USA 1957)

The Attraction of Onlookers: Aberfan – An Anatomy of a Welsh Village
2008
Five screen video projection. Edition 1/3
Purchased with the assistance of Derek Williams Trust 2010
NMW A 29485

On 21 October 1966 in the village of Aberfan in south Wales a colliery waste tip slid down the mountainside and engulfed Pantglas Junior School. In total 144 people – 28 adults and 116 children – lost their lives. In 2006, to mark the fortieth anniversary of the disaster, the New York-based artist Shimon Attie was invited to Aberfan by BBC Wales to make a work of art.

Attie developed this video installation as a contribution to the village's desire to move on from the tragic events of that day. After gaining the trust of the community, he developed ideas for the work through dialogue and discussion. Creating a temporary studio in the chapel, Attie embarked on an ambitious project to represent a cross-section of the community.

Individuals, groups and families were invited to the studio where they were filmed assuming static poses that reflect their social or occupational roles within the community: the ex-coal miner, the boxer, the minister, the traffic warden and so on. Attie then filmed them on an unseen revolving stage using dramatic lighting to create light and shadow reminiscent of Old Master paintings. In the final installation these figures are projected near life-size on five screens that can be arranged in a number of different configurations.

Accompanied by music the figures appear in space then disappear. The work has a rhythm and a pace that builds through its duration. In the final section all the figures appear at once so that the viewer is completely surrounded by the people of Aberfan. The making of the work was the subject of a BBC documentary, *An American in Aberfan*, in 2006. *NT*

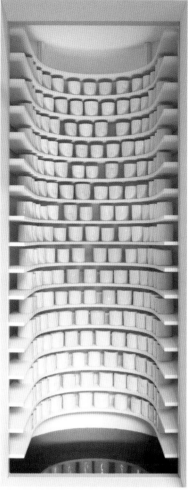

© Edmund de Waal

149. Edmund de Waal
(b. Nottingham 1964)

Porcelain Wall
2005 and 2007

222 pots, porcelain with various glazes, each approximately 10 x 10 x 10cm

Purchased with assistance from the Colwinston Charitable Trust, the Derek Williams Trust and the Art Fund (167 pots, 2005); given by Edmund de Waal (55 pots, 2007)

NMW A 38101

De Waal created this installation for the exhibition *Arcanum: mapping 18th-century European porcelain* at National Museum Cardiff in 2005. In it he juxtaposed new work of his own with arrangements of historic porcelain from the collection given to the Museum by Wilfred de Winton in the early twentieth century.

The wall is the artist's response to his study of the de Winton collection, to the stories embodied within the objects, to the mind of the collector, to the history of the collection itself. Following the gift of additional pots to allow it to be reinstalled in the Museum, it comprises over two hundred cylindrical vessels. Each pot is glazed from a palette of seventeen different white glazes developed during the project. Each is also impressed on the side with grouped or single marks that echo de Winton's fascination with factory marks.

De Waal says that the work 'has a perverse logic to it, a catalogue of marks and indentations, a spectrum of different whites.' It is effectively a personal taxonomy in dialogue with early European porcelain's varying hues, with the markings that elucidate an object's history and with the taxonomy of decorative styles that underpinned de Winton's collection. It is also a contemporary take on the eighteenth-century tradition of architectural display of porcelain.

De Waal has moved away from the 'Anglo-Oriental' school of studio pottery into which he was apprenticed. Having redefined the legacy of its father figure Bernard Leach in a ground-breaking biography in 1998, he is now also redefining the ways in which ceramics are located and viewed, exploring, in his words, 'the intersection between architecture, ceramics and sculptural installation'. *AR*

150. Elizabeth Fritsch
(b. Oswestry, Shropshire 1940)

Blown-away Vase, Over the Edge, Firework XII
2008
Hand-built stoneware, coloured matt slips, height: 40.7cm

Vase: Water of Greenness
2008
Hand-built stoneware, coloured matt slips, height: 34.5cm

Purchased with assistance from the Derek Williams Trust and the Art Fund, 2009
NMW A 39102, 39103

A fresco-like surface texture and depth of rich colour give Elizabeth Fritsch's hand-built vessels an immediate tactile and visual appeal. They are, however, objects of immense complexity, informed by a formidable range of intellectual interests, from musical theory and mathematics to literature, mythology and geology.

Fritsch also explores the paradoxes that arise when the illusory space created by painting on a surface interacts with the real space occupied by a three-dimensional object. These apparently fully rounded vases are in fact flattened representations of vessels, ambiguous objects in '2½ dimensions'. The interaction between form and surface is based on musical principles. For Fritsch, herself a proficient musician, the complex painted rhythm figures 'correspond to tempo and rhythm in music' and are modified by and combine with the form.

Firework XII's blue-black ground symbolises the night sky. Scattered particles with white flashes appear to float free in space within the vessel, an illusion that dematerialises its surface and challenges our perception of reality.

Water of Greenness is a name used in the ancient Egyptian Pyramid Texts for Osiris, god of the afterlife and fertility. The vessel therefore alludes to death though, for Fritsch, 'not as a morbid finality but as a source for imaginative ideas'.

Fritsch is the pre-eminent ceramic artist of Welsh origin and perhaps the most important potter of her generation. Influenced by the teaching of Hans Coper (see no. 132), she was the first of a generation of outstanding ceramicists to graduate from the Royal College of Art in the early 1970s. Leading a move away from the dominant wheel-thrown, functional approach to ceramics, she helped to redefine the parameters of the craft ceramics movement. *AR*

Further reading

Building a national art collection

Bala, Iwan (ed.), *Certain Welsh Artists: Custodial Aesthetics in Contemporary Welsh Art*, Seren, 1999

Evans, Mark, *The Derek Williams Collection at the National Museum of Wales*, National Museum of Wales, 1989

Evans, Mark and Fairclough, Oliver, *A Companion Guide to the National Art Gallery,* National Museum of Wales, 1993 and 1997

Fairclough, Oliver (ed.), *'Things of Beauty': What two sisters did for Wales*, National Museum Wales Books, 2007

Fairclough, Oliver and Dawkes, Bryony, *Tuner to Cézanne: Masterpieces from the Davies Collection*, Hudson Hills Press, 2009

Gibbs, John Morel, *James Pyke Thompson: The Turner House, Penarth, 1888-1988*, National Museum of Wales, 1990

Ingamells, John, *The Davies Collection of French Art*, National Museum of Wales, 1967

Lord, Peter, *The Visual Culture of Wales: The Industrial Society*, University of Wales Press, 1998

Lord, Peter, *The Visual Culture of Wales: Imaging the Nation*, University of Wales Press, 2000

Marshall, T. Pirsig, *A Catalogue of the Derek Williams Trust Collection 1993-2006*, Derek Williams Trust, 2007

McIntyre, Bethany, *Sisters Select: Works on Paper from the Davies Collection*, National Museum Wales Books, 2000

Rowan, Eric and Stewart, Carolyn, *An Elusive Tradition: Art and Society in Wales 1870-1950*, University of Wales Press, 2002

Sixteenth and seventeenth-century art

Blunt, Anthony, *The Paintings of Nicolas Poussin*, Phaidon, 1966

Les Frères Le Nain, Grand Palais, 1978

Glanville, Philippa, *Silver in Tudor and Early Stuart England*, Victoria and Albert Museum, 1990

The Glory of the Golden Age: Dutch art of the 17th century, Waanders Publishers and Rijksmuseum Amsterdam, 2000

Hearn, Karen (ed.), *Dynasties: Painting in Tudor and Jacobean England, 1530-1630*, Tate, 1995

Harris, A. Sutherland, *Andrea Sacchi*, Phaidon, 1977

Humfrey, Peter, *Cima da Conegliano*, Cambridge University Press, 1983

Thornton, Dora and Wilson, Timothy, *Italian Renaissance Ceramics: a catalogue of the British Museum collection*, British Museum, 2009

Wine, Humphrey, *Claude: The Poetic Landscape*, National Gallery, 1994

Eighteenth-century art

Adams, Elizabeth, *Chelsea Porcelain*, Barrie & Jenkins, 1987

Clark, Anthony M., *Pompeo Batoni: A Complete Catalogue of his Works*, Phaidon, 1985

Hayes, John, *The Landscape Paintings of Thomas Gainsborough*, Sotheby's, 1983

Manners and Morals, Hogarth and British Paintings 1700-1760, exh. cat., Tate Gallery, 1987

Mannings, David, *Sir Joshua Reynolds: A Complete Catalogue of his Paintings*, Yale University Press, 2000

Pietsch, Ulrich and Banz, Claudia, *Triumph of the Blue Swords: Meissen Porcelain for Aristocracy and Bourgeoisie*, Staatliche Kunstsammlungen Dresden, 2010

Solkin, David H. (ed.), *Richard Wilson*, Tate Gallery, 1982

Sumner, Ann and Smith, Greg (eds), *Thomas Jones 1742-1803: An Artist Rediscovered*, Yale University Press, 2003

Cato, M. Wynn, *The Life and Works of William Parry ARA 1743-1791*, the author, 2008

Wilton, Andrew and Bignamini, Ilaria, *Grand Tour: The Lure of Italy in the Eighteenth Century*, Tate, 1996

Nineteenth-century art

Crook, J. Mordaunt, *William Burges and the High Victorian Dream*, Murray, 1981

Dorment, Richard, *Alfred Gilbert*, Yale University Press, 1985

Edward Burne-Jones: The Earthly Paradise, exh. cat., Staatsgalerie Stuttgart & Kunstmuseum Bern, 2009

Elsen, Albert E. and Jamison, Rosalyn Frankel, *Rodin's Art: The Rodin Collection of the Iris & B. Gerald Cantor Center for Visual Arts at Stanford University*, Oxford University Press: New York, 2003

Jones, A. E. and Joseph, Leslie, *Swansea Porcelain: Shapes & Decoration*, D. Brown, 1988

Kelly, Franklin and Warrell, Ian, *J.M.W. Turner*, Tate, 2007

Matyjaszkiewicz, Krystyna (ed.), *James Tissot*, Phaidon, 1984

McIntyre, Bethany, *Victorian Visions: Pre-Raphaelite Drawings and Watercolours from the National Museums & Galleries of Wales*, International Arts & Artists, 2003

Nance, E. Morton, *The Pottery and Porcelain of Swansea and Nantgarw*, Batsford. 1942

Pearson, Fiona, *Goscombe John at the National Museum of Wales*, National Museum of Wales, 1979

Pissarro, Joachim, *Monet's Cathedral: Rouen, 1892-1894*, Pavilion Books, 1990

Riopelle, Christopher and Sumner, Ann, *Sisley in England and Wales*, National Gallery, 2009

Spencer-Longhurst, Paul, *The Blue Bower: Rossetti in the 1860s*, Scala, 2010

Sumner, Ann (ed.), *Colour and Light: Fifty Impressionist and Post-Impressionist Works at the National Museum of Wales*, National Museum Wales Books, 2005

Wilcox, Scott, *Sun Wind and Rain: The Art of David Cox*, Yale University Press, 2008

Art from the first half of the twentieth century

Cardew, Michael, *A Pioneer Potter: An Autobiography*, Collins, 1988

Cooper, Emmanuel, *Bernard Leach, Life & Work*, Yale University Press, 2003

Cork, Richard, *Jacob Epstein*, Tate, 1999

Dawkes, Bryony and Meyrick, Robert, *Radical Visions: British Art 1910-1950*, Oriel Davies Gallery, 2006

Edwards, Paul and others, *Wyndham Lewis (1882-1957)*, Fundacion Juan March, 2010

Fischer, Hartwig and Rainbird, Sean (eds), *Kandinsky: the Path to Abstraction 1902-1922*, Tate, 2006

Jenkins, D. Fraser, *J. D. Innes at the National Museum of Wales*, National Museum of Wales, 1975

Jenkins, D. Fraser and Spalding, Frances, *John Piper in the 1930s: Abstraction on the Beach*, Merrell, 2003

Jenkins, D. Fraser and Stephens Chris, *Gwen John and Augustus John*, Tate, 2004

Gooding, Mel, *Ceri Richards*, Cameron & Hollis, 2002

Langdale, Cecily, *Gwen John*, Yale University Press, 1987

McCully, Marilyn, *Picasso: Painter and Sculptor in Clay*, Royal Academy, 1998

Miles, Jonathan and Shiel, Derek, *David Jones: the Maker Unmade*, Seren, 1995

Parton, Anthony, *Goncharova: The Art and Design of Natalia Goncharova*, Antique Collectors Club Ltd, 2010

Silber, Evelyn, *Gaudier-Brzeska: Life and Art*, Thames and Hudson, 1996

Tufnell, Ben (ed.), *Cedric Morris and Lett Haines: Teaching Art and Life*, Norfolk Museums & Archaeology Service and National Museum Wales Books, 2002

Art after 1950

Alston, David and others, *Process: Explorations of the Work of Tim Davies*, Seren, 2002

Alston, David, Morris, Lynda and Curtis, Tony, *The Painter's Quarry: The Art of Peter Prendergast*, Seren, 2006

Attie, Shimon, *The Attraction of Onlookers: Aberfan: An Anatomy of a Welsh Village*, Parthian Books, 2008

Birks, Tony, *Hans Coper*, Harper & Row, 1983

Cooper, Emmanuel and Fielding, Amanda *Walter Keeler*, Ruthin Craft Centre, 2004

Elizabeth Fritsch, The Fine Art Society/Joanna Bird Pottery, London, 2008

Hammer, Martin, *Bacon and Sutherland*, Yale University Press, 2005

Hughes, Robert, *Lucian Freud: Paintings*, Thames & Hudson, 1989

Hurn, David and Grafik, Clare, *I'm a Real Photographer: Keith Arnatt Photographs 1974-2002*, Chris Boot Ltd/The Photographers' Gallery, 2007

Juncosa, Enrique (ed.), *Barry Flanagan Sculpture: 1965-2005*, Irish Museum of Modern Art, 2006

Koplos, Janet and others, *Betty Woodman*, The Monacelli Press, 2006

Kudielka, Robert (ed.), *The Eye's Mind: Bridget Riley, Collected Writings 1965-2009*, Thames and Hudson, 2009

Lampert, Catherine and Rosenthal, Norman, *Frank Auerbach, Paintings and drawings 1954-2001*, Royal Academy of Arts, 2001

Rossiter, Peter, Johnson, Nichola and Podro, Michael, *Martin Bloch: A Painter's Painter*, Sainsbury Centre for Visual Arts, 2007

Sayle, Murray and Griffiths, P. Jones, *Dark Odyssey: Philip Jones Griffiths*, Aperture Foundation, National Museum of Wales, 1996

Stephens, Chris, *Barbara Hepworth: Centenary*, Tate, 2003

Tooby, Michael and Holman, Martin, *Terry Setch: A Retrospective*, University of Wales Institute, 2001

de Waal, Edmund and others, *Arcanum: mapping 18th-century European porcelain*, National Museum Wales Books, 2005

Notes on contributors

Rachel Conroy
Assistant Curator of Applied Art. Works across the breadth of the applied art collection. Particular interests are historic metalwork and contemporary silver.

Bryony Dawkes
Curator of Partnership Projects. Works across the whole range of the art collections on collaborative projects with partner venues. Special interests are twentieth-century art and interdisciplinarity.

Oliver Fairclough
Keeper of Art at Amgueddfa Cymru. Special interests include art collections and artists in Wales, the art of the British landscape, British and European ceramics and silver and Welsh porcelain.

Rachel Flynn
AHRC Collaborative Doctoral Award student. Researching Graham Sutherland in a partnership between Amgueddfa Cymru and the University of Bristol.

Beth McIntyre
Curator of Prints & Drawings. Works on the collection of watercolours, drawings, prints and photographs dating from the sixteenth century to the present day. Special interests are British landscape painting, early twentieth-century British art, Gwen and Augustus John and artists' sketchbooks.

Melissa Munro
Derek Williams Curator of Modern and Contemporary Art. Works on the post-1900 art collections of the Derek Williams Trust and Amgueddfa Cymru. Special interests are Dada, Surrealism and Neo-Romanticism.

Anne Pritchard
Assistant Curator of Historic Art. Works on the collections of paintings and sculpture from before 1900. Special interests are nineteenth-century French and Impressionist art.

Andrew Renton
Head of Applied Art. Works on collections dating from antiquity to the present day, with particular emphasis on Welsh and other ceramics of the eighteenth and early nineteenth centuries and on modern and contemporary applied art.

Nicholas Thornton
Head of Modern & Contemporary Art. Works on the research and display of the fine art collections from 1900 to the present day. Special interests include post-war British art and contemporary practice in Wales.

Michael Tooby
Director of Learning, Programmes & Development. Has worked on the National Museum of Art development since initiating the consultation on the display of visual arts in Wales, published in the document *Views of the Future*, in 2001.

Charlotte Topsfield
Assistant Curator of Prints & Drawings. Works across the range of the works on paper collection, including drawings, watercolours, prints, photographs and miniatures and archives. Special interest is early twentieth-century British art.